The Infinite Voyage

The Infinite Voyage

Man's Future in Space

POUL ANDERSON

CROWELL-COLLIER PRESS
COLLIER-MACMILLAN LIMITED / LONDON

Library of Congress Catalog Card Number: 69–10533

The Macmillan Company
Collier-Macmillan Canada Ltd., Toronto, Ontario
Printed in the United States of America

FIRST PRINTING

PICTURE CREDITS

Culver Pictures, Inc., 9; Historical Pictures Service—Chicago, 4, 5, 16, 148–49; Mount Wilson and Palomar Observatories, title page, ix, 105, 110, 118, 121, 126–27, 130, 144–45; NASA, 26, 28, 43, 47, 49, 52, 54, 55, 57, 62; United Press International Photo, 22, 29, 37, 40, 45, 67, 69, 71, 78, 83, 102, 150–51.

To Per and Lene Bertelsen
—who will inherit the space age—
and, of course, also to their parents

Foreword

Man has always been an adventurer. Long before history was written, heroes were seeking new lands. Armed with nothing better than fire and flint, they dared unknown forests and hunted the mammoth across the Ice Age tundra. Others crossed to America, Australia, and the remotest Pacific islands.

Everywhere on Earth, myth and legend and chronicle have honored the great adventurers. One of the oldest stories is the Egyptian tale of Sinuhe the sailor. It was later adapted by the Arabs, who were fearless navigators themselves. Thus we know the sailor best as Sinbad. The Greeks told of Odysseus, the Hindus of Sanudasa, the Irish of St. Brendan, the Polynesians of Maui—and so on through a nearly endless list.

Travel and exploration also filled real life. What glamour there is in the sea kings of ancient Crete, the merchant skippers of Phoenicia, the Romans who traded as far as Java, the Vikings, the Crusaders, Marco Polo, and a thousand more! The greatest epic of all, of course, began with Columbus. In the next four centuries, the entire world was opened up. It was a grand time to be alive for any young man with fire in his blood.

We do not yet lack frontiers, even on this planet. Three-fourths of its surface is covered by ocean, a vast mysterious kingdom that we have scarcely begun to explore. Strange things may still be found on land, in the Antarctic or a tropical rain forest. In quiet laboratories, and amidst whirring computers, the search goes on too: for science is itself a voyage of discovery, and one which may never have an end.

But we are not satisfied. We want the utterly new, the kind of experience that Cortez had when he first saw Mexico City or Livingstone at Victoria Falls. It is good to gain understanding of Earth. Yet at night we look upward. A full moon rises opposite white Venus, Mars glowers, Jupiter gleams, whole worlds lie out there. And past them beckon the uncountable stars, each a sun. Surely among them are new earths. Who can foresee what may be found, gotten, learned, what deeds may be done and what songs be sung, on the other side of our sky?

Man, the wanderer, is outward bound again.

That will not be an easy quest. A short book like this cannot begin to tell the heartbreaking difficulties and dangers. Some have been met and conquered; others remain; others lurk in the future, unknown until we stumble upon them.

But we must not grow impatient or fearful. Our ancestors did not reach the ends of their own world easily. We, today, are the first into cosmic space. Those who come after us will go farther, faster, because of what we have done. Ours is the toil of the trail-breaker. But ours, too, is his glory.

What may we actually expect to see while we are alive? What reward will we personally reap? The answer depends largely on us. The harder we try, the more we can win. Now suppose we do mount a bold, unflagging attempt to explore the universe. How far can we hope to get? What might we come upon? How might

The uncountable stars beckon man the wanderer to an infinite voyage.

it affect our daily life at home? What could happen along the way?

This book will try to answer those questions. The answers will be incomplete, partly for lack of space, partly because nobody knows everything—not by a long shot. But we can look briefly at what has already happened, what is going on, and what will probably take place in the next fifty years or so. At the end, we can look deeper into time and space, toward the goals of a future more distant. And we can rejoice that we are the first generation of cosmic man.

Contents

The Infinite Voyage

CHAPTER 1

The Greatest Adventure

The idea of new frontiers in the heavens is prehistorically old. As far back as records go, and no doubt much further than that, mankind has believed in celestial beings. Gods, angels, dragons, whatever they were, were supposed to live above the clouds and occasionally descend to earth.

Perhaps—just barely perhaps—some of these stories hold a kernel of truth. Could visitors from other planets be responsible? A few accounts are oddly suggestive. For example, there is the Sumerian legend of the demigod Oannes, who did not look like a human being, but who taught men the arts of civilization. One of the visions of the prophet Ezekiel, as related in the Bible, reads as if it might be an attempt to describe a spaceship and its alien crew. Of course, this is sheer speculation, and in all likelihood is wrong. Imagination alone can easily have brought forth those tales. Later on, though, we shall think a little more carefully about the possibility of intelligent creatures who can travel between the stars.

The realms from which the powerful ones came were always taken to be supernatural. Nobody thought that worlds akin to ours might exist elsewhere or that men might reach them by normal means. That realization had to wait until it was learned that Earth was only another planet and that the stars were only other suns.

More than 3000 years before Christ, the Sumerians and their Babylonian successors, in what is now Iraq, charted the skies with care and patience. They noticed that certain points of light did not stay fixed in any single constellation but moved. Such strange behavior made the priest-astronomers think that these objects must be associated with the gods, might in a sense *be* gods. They named them accordingly. But if a god was in the sky, was he not there for a purpose? From this reasoning the concepts of astrology developed, the belief that the stars and planets control our lives. The superstition spread as far as China, where the Imperial court supported official astrologers until modern times. In fact, there remain many believers in astrology today.

The Greeks were the first true astronomers, that is, men who studied the heavens with the aim of finding sensible explanations for what they saw. As early as 300 B.C. they had decided Earth must be round. A century later, Eratosthenes estimated its size quite accurately, using the difference in altitude of the sun at noon on the same day in two cities, one of which was a known distance north of the other. Later his figure was discarded in favor of a smaller one. Columbus used the incorrect figure when he reasoned that it should be possible to reach the East by sailing west. Maybe we should be thankful that he did not know how far off Asia really was!

The question remained, however, as to whether or not Earth

was the fixed center of the universe. It looked as if sun, moon, and stars wheeled around us. On the other hand, there were the puzzling planets (the word is Greek and means "wanderer"). Their motions back and forth were hard to fit into any such scheme. Hence the philosopher Aristarchus declared about 270 B.C. that everything actually circles the sun, except for the moon that does turn around Earth and the stars that are fixed in place.

His idea was destroyed in approximately 150 B.C., together with the findings of Eratosthenes. The man who did this was actually a first-rate astronomer, named Hipparchus. He went back to the concept of a geocentric—Earth-centered—universe, arguing that if Earth swings about the sun, the stars ought to show parallax. That is, when we look at a star from opposite sides of Earth's orbit, it ought to appear in two different positions, just as a tree seems to move when we go past it. Since we do not find any stellar parallax, Hipparchus said, our world must be motionless.

Actually, the parallax is there. But the stars are so far away that it is very small. Only the most sensitive modern instruments can measure it directly, and they can only do so for the nearest ones. We can scarcely blame Hipparchus for not imagining such abyssal distances.

By A.D. 150 the geocentric universe was fully accepted. At that time a scholar named Ptolemy wrote a book that summarized astronomical knowledge. We know it today by its Arabic title, the Almagest. For centuries it was taken as the final word on its subject. Therefore the geocentric system is called the Ptolemaic.

True, a generation earlier, the historian Plutarch had described the moon as being like a small Earth. And in the lifetime of the Almagest's author, the satirist Lucian told two stories about lunar voyages. His characters did not use what we would call a practical method. In one book, a ship is whirled aloft by a

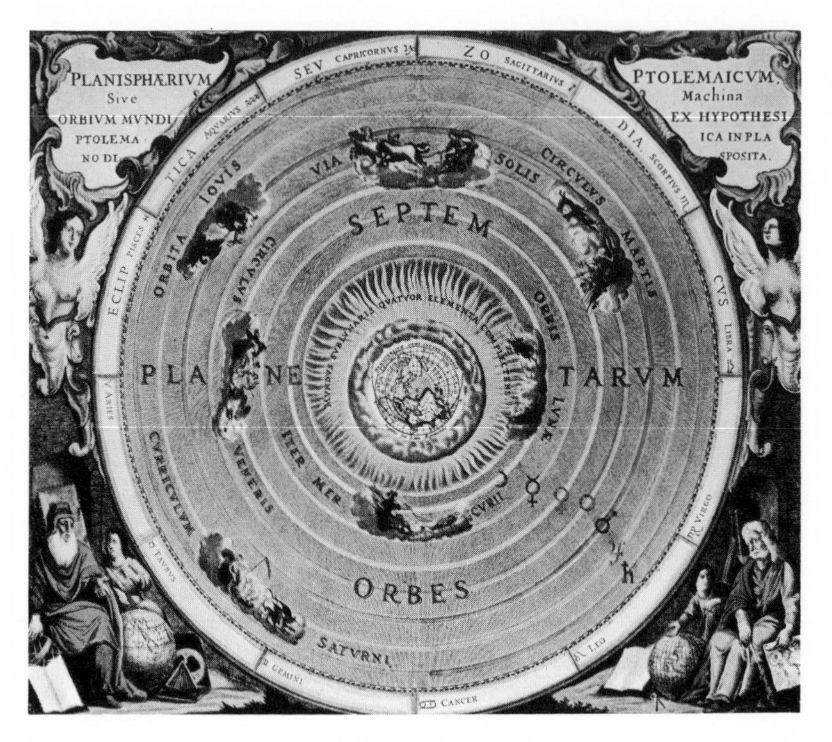

This seventeenth-century print depicts the Ptolemaic system: the universe is centered around Earth.

hurricane; in the other, the hero flies by means of wings strapped to his arms. But at least the idea of many worlds was still alive.

It died with the Roman Empire. Its ghost haunted the Middle Ages, though wanly. A few thinkers suggested that God was too powerful and too good to have created just one globe. In general, however, ideas about the heavenly bodies were ruled by astrology and the Almagest. Sun, moon, planets, and stars were supposed to be lights for the benefit of man, also having occult influences upon him, and Earth was believed to be at the middle of all things.

As time went on, more and more people studied the heavens with greater and greater care. This was partly because astrologers needed to know how the planets behaved, but probably more of the effort was for the benefit of navigation, as ships

The Copernican system showed the planets revolving around the sun in perfect, circular orbits.

made ever-longer voyages. Surely some of it was due to the same curiosity that had once animated the Greeks.

Facts and figures piled up. Less and less could they be squared with simple rotations in a geocentric system. Rather, men had to depict the heavenly bodies as following extremely complicated tracks, circles upon circles upon circles. By the thirteenth century, astronomical concepts had grown so fantastic that King Alfonso X of Castile remarked, "If I had been there at the time of creation, I could have given the Creator some good advice."

Nevertheless, it was not until 1543 that anyone openly challenged Ptolemy. In that year, Nicholas Copernicus of Poland published a book. It was in Latin, like all scholarly works of that time; the title was *De Revolutionibus Orbium Coelestium* (On the Revolutions of the Heavenly Bodies). The text showed how much easier and more natural it would be to adopt the heliocentric—sun-centered—universe of Hipparchus. So many powerful interests—astrological, intellectual, and religious—were now involved with the geocentric idea that Copernicus waited to have his book printed until he was safely on his deathbed. It roused a storm of controversy.

Three years later, Tycho Brahe was born in Denmark. He became a great scientist. Although the telescope had not yet been invented, he compiled so many exact observations that the Ptolemaic theory could no longer stand before them. Ironically, he himself never accepted this, and died believing in a fixed Earth.

It remained for his German pupil Johann Kepler to see what the data really meant. An odd, nervous man, Kepler was a court astrologer for a while. He tried to work out a system wherein the skies were arranged according to a mystical geometry. But his respect for facts, and his insight, were too strong. In 1609 he published his *Astronomia Nova* (New Astronomy), which completed the work of Copernicus.

Copernicus had never shaken off the ancient idea that celestial motions must be circular because the circle is the perfect figure. And so to explain the behavior of the planets, he was forced to keep some of the old complicated loops in their orbits. Kepler proved that this was not necessary. If the planets move, not in circles but in ellipses, according to certain laws he discovered, we can account for everything we see in a clear and simple way.

Kepler also wrote the first interplanetary story since Lucian. His book *Somnium* (Sleep) relates a dream in which he sees a young man carried to the moon by a friendly demon. The moon is no magical realm but a perfectly natural place like Earth, although different in most of its features.

Meanwhile, the telescope had appeared and the Italian Galileo

Galilei had turned it on the skies. There he found that the moon has mountains, that Jupiter has satellites, that there are dark spots upon the supposedly unblemished sun—in short, he found complete worlds other than our own. The idea was so shocking that he got into deep trouble for announcing it. While the authorities were willing to let him use Copernican ideas as an aid to calculating the motions of the heavenly bodies, he was forced to deny that these ideas described anything real.

But gradually, as more and more people accumulated more and more observations, it came to be accepted that Copernicus, Kepler, and Galileo had discovered important truths.

In 1642, the year of Galileo's death, Isaac Newton was born in England. This was one of the towering geniuses of all time. Almost single-handed, he laid the foundations of modern physical science. By his laws of motion and gravitation, he showed *why* the planets move as Kepler said. By stating that these laws are universal, he struck down the last excuse for believing that Earth is anything special or that supernatural things can be seen in the heavens. Other worlds may be strange indeed, but they are as real as the one that we stand on, governed by the same principles. We can come to know them.

Newton's work showed what had not been clear before, that there cannot be any air between the planets. Otherwise friction would soon make them fall into the sun. This undermined several books that were being written in that era, whose characters travel beyond Earth in vehicles drawn by birds and the like. At the same time, as we shall see later, Newton's third law of motion pointed toward the proper means for crossing space.

Interestingly enough, the method had already been proposed. In 1649 the Frenchman Cyrano de Bergerac wrote a story whose hero makes such a voyage in a box driven by large rockets. But we must admit that when he created the first fictional rocket-ship, he did not understand what he was doing. In other interplanetary tales, he used devices that are flatly impossible.

Romances of that kind became popular in the eighteenth and nineteenth centuries, as knowledge of the new astronomy spread among educated people. For instance, Voltaire wrote *Micromégas,* in which Earth is visited by an inhabitant of Saturn and his traveling companion from the star Sirius. In *From the Earth to the Moon,* Jules Verne described how a spaceship was propelled. Unfortunately, it was by a gigantic cannon. This wouldn't work. If nothing else, the impact as the shell was fired would kill the passengers. But at least Verne did think of the problem as one that would be solved by engineers. H. G. Wells, in *The First Men in the Moon* and *The War of the Worlds,* took less interest in practical questions. In fact, neither of his space travel stories uses a workable method.

Meanwhile, the astronomers were making exciting discoveries. For a while it looked as if Mars might well be inhabited by thinking creatures. Many ideas were suggested for communicating with them. One was by Karl Friedrich Gauss, the leading mathematician of the nineteenth century. Let forest and grainfields be planted in Siberia, he said, making continent-sized geometrical figures that the Martians could recognize. Then they would know that intelligent beings live on Earth and would probably respond. Needless to say, the project was never carried out. But as late as 1927, serious efforts were made by governments to detect any radio signals that might be coming from the red planet.

Space travel romances like Jules Verne's From the Earth to the Moon *described many kinds of spaceships. Verne's projectile was propelled by a gigantic cannon.*

There was no success. It did not discourage the dreamers. Any number of short stories and novels were written about expeditions to the planets. But then the scientists decided once for all that, whatever might exist elsewhere, Earth is the only child of Sol on which our kind of life can flourish. Accordingly, the science fiction writers have moved most of their story settings farther off. On the imaginary worlds of distant stars, heroes may do as they choose without fear of contradiction.

But for how long? When will reality again catch up with imagination? And may it not prove more wonderful? How can we leave this planet and find out?

CHAPTER 2

The Romance of the Rocket

Not many years ago, a surprising number of people still claimed that it was impossible to send a rocket through airless space. "What would it push against?" they asked. Today, when these machines operate almost routinely beyond the atmosphere, you seldom hear the question. But no doubt many remain puzzled as to why the method works.

The answer lies in Newton's third law of motion. The rocket, like any material object, obeys all three of Newton's laws. They are not hard to understand.

First law: every body persists in a state of rest or of uniform motion unless it is acted on by a force. That is, a body that is not moving does not start to move without some kind of push or pull. A stone lying on the ground will continue to lie there until someone or something picks it up, or rolls it, or works on it in some other way. A man seated in a chair will continue to sit there until he pushes himself up with his own muscles, or he is pulled up, or something else of that nature happens.

Likewise, once a body is moving in a straight line, it will keep on moving in that same direction and at that same speed until a force acts on it. A thrown baseball falls to the ground because of the pull of gravity. Were there no gravity (and no friction with air), it would fly forever on an unchanging course, at an unchanging speed.

The mass of a body—the total amount of matter in it—multiplied by its velocity is called its momentum. For instance, a 3-pound stone moving at 10 feet per second has a momentum of 3 times 10, or 30 pound-feet per second.

Second law: when a force acts on a body, the rate of change of momentum is in proportion to the size of the force, and in the same direction as the force. Thus, when you pick up a ball from the ground, it rises because you are lifting it upward. When you shove it along the ground, it does not rise, but moves in the direction of your push. The harder you lift or shove, the faster the ball moves. If one ball was hit twice as hard as another, it would take off with exactly twice the speed, provided both had the same mass.

Momentum is mass times velocity. Velocity is not the same as speed. It is speed in a given *direction.* To say you are driving at a speed of 60 miles per hour obviously means less than to say you are driving with a velocity of 60 miles per hour northward.

It takes force to change the direction of a moving object just as it does to change its speed. You can feel this kind of pressure when a car goes around a curve as much as when it speeds up or slows down. Any change in velocity is called an "acceleration." An acceleration may be a change in speed, in direction, or both. Since spaceships are often under high accelerations, astronauts are very conscious of the forces involved.

Third law: to every action there is an equal and opposite reaction. Whenever and wherever a force is applied, another force operates that is precisely as strong and works in precisely the opposite direction. The first force is called the action, the second the reaction. For instance, when the force of expanding gases accelerates a bullet from the muzzle of a gun, it also accelerates the gun against the person who is shooting. Or when you jump from a boat on water, the boat is pushed backward as you spring forward.

Some people might wonder why a car or an airplane does not behave similarly when the passengers step out. The reason is that these heavy vehicles are well anchored to the ground by friction. In such cases, not only the vehicle but the whole planet—or, at least, a good part of the local landscape—moves away in reaction. Its mass is so great, however, that this motion is too small to detect.

We can make that clearer by returning to the gun. Suppose it fires a bullet weighing $\frac{1}{50}$ of a pound at 2,000 feet per second. The force of the action then gives this bullet a momentum of $\frac{1}{50}$ times 2,000 or 40 pound-feet per second. Reaction makes the gun recoil with the same value of momentum in the opposite direction from the bullet. But if it is a rifle weighing 10 pounds, it picks up only 4 feet per second in order to come out with that value of 40.

Since Earth has a mass of well over six billion trillion tons, we can readily see why it does not recoil much from us!

Any device that produces movement by accelerating mass in the opposite direction may be called a reaction motor. A gun could be put in this class, although the "kick" is not wanted. Probably the simplest reaction motor is a toy balloon. When it is blown up and closed, the air inside presses equally outward in all directions. So there is no net force and nothing happens.

But if we open the balloon, air rushes out. The inside pressure directly opposite the hole is now unbalanced. Obedient to the force acting upon it, the balloon flies.

These examples ought to make it plain that a gun will recoil or an opened toy balloon will take off whether or not we have an atmosphere around them. They don't need anything except themselves to "push against." Indeed, a rocket works best in a vacuum, where it is not hampered by wind and friction.

To be exact, we should remark that this is not true of every reaction motor. The jets on an airplane work by drawing in the surrounding air, heating it by the flames of burning fuel, and blowing it out backward. So they would be helpless in space. A rocket takes everything that it needs along with it.

Discounting things like oars, the first reaction motors that we know of were made by the early Greeks. They were little more than toys, though intended to impress worshipers in the temples. About 360 B.C., Archytas fashioned a wooden pigeon which flew at the end of a string, doubtless by means of a steam jet. Not long afterward, Heron of Alexandria created the aeolipile. This was a hollow sphere mounted on pivots and filled with water. When a fire was lit beneath, the water boiled, steam blew out of two nozzles pointed opposite to each other, and the aeolipile spun around. A version of this gadget is in use today as the common lawn sprinkler.

The rocket itself originally came from China. Just when it was invented there is unknown. A chronicle dates its first serious use at A.D. 1232 In that year, Mongols led by a son of Genghis Khan were besieging the city of Kai-fung-fu. The Chinese defenders not only used bombs filled with gunpowder against them, but shot "arrows of flying fire." These were evidently little rockets, attached to feathered sticks which helped them fly straight through the air. They carried some kind of charge that scattered flames when it struck. Though they gave the Mongols a good deal of trouble, they did not prevent the country from being overrun. Thereafter the Chinese simply used rockets as fireworks.

Nevertheless, the invention was taken up by the Arabs, and the people of India and Europe learned about it from them. This did not take long either. During the thirteenth century, the Englishman Roger Bacon and the German Albertus Magnus set down formulas for gunpowder. It powered not only the clumsy cannon of the time, but rockets as well. The latter are mentioned in a record for the year 1258, and were definitely used in battle in the Mediterranean area by 1379. So, strange as it seems, the armored, plumed, sword- and lance-wielding knights of the Middle Ages occasionally confronted guided missiles!

Of course, these were small and crude. Improved artillery and hand guns drove them off the field in a couple of centuries. They lasted a while longer in naval warfare, setting enemy ships afire. And they have remained good for signaling and festive displays to the present day.

In A.D. 1500, China saw another brief, unsuccessful bit of pioneering. An official named Wan-Hu longed to fly. He fastened two large kites in a light framework to a kind of saddle where he was to sit and put forty-seven large rockets at different places on this frame. At a signal, his coolies put torches to the fuses. The bold Wan-Hu and his craft vanished in a burst of flame and smoke. It would be pleasant to believe that he reached the moon, but no doubt he only went to his Confucian reward.

Although some experimentation continued in Europe, the Western world took little further interest in rocketry until 1800. Several years before then, the British in India had suffered bad defeats at the hands of the Mogul sultan Tippoo Sahib. Building on the work of his father, this ruler gave his army a rocket corps numbering 5,000 men. Its weapons had tubes of iron, not pasteboard, with 10-foot guiding poles, and weighed up to 12 pounds. While not as accurate as artillery, they were cheaper to make and

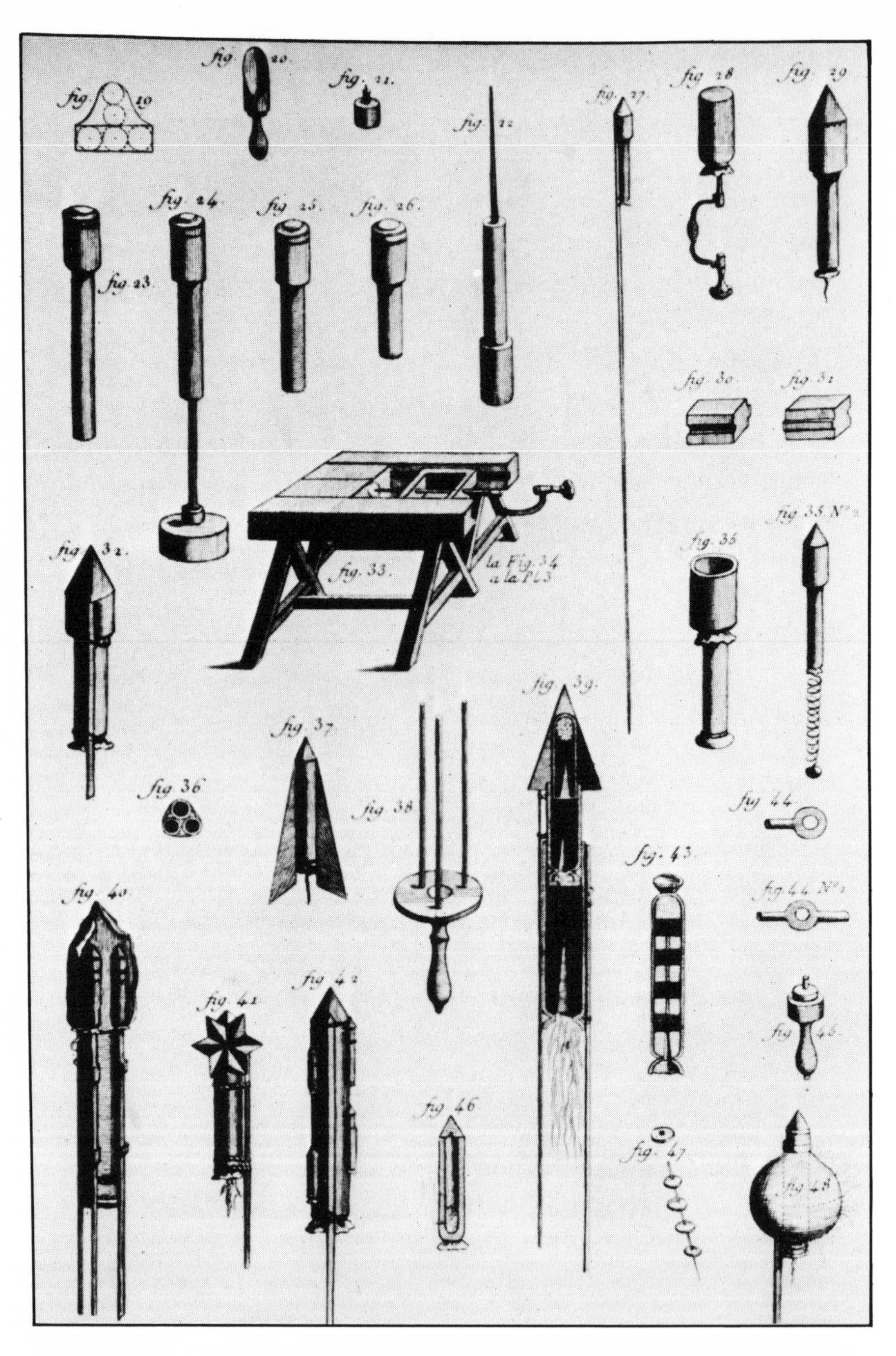

A variety of eighteenth-century rockets and rocket tools from Diderot's Encyclopedia. *Figure 39 is a three-stage rocket.*

easier to transport. Hence, they could be used in great salvos that were particularly hard on opposing cavalry.

An Englishman named William Congreve took the lesson to heart and began developing improved missiles of that type. Some weighed over 40 pounds. Much of this mass was solid fuel; but they could deliver up to 18 pounds of bomb or shot at ranges up to nearly 2 miles. Furthermore, they did not need the heavy structure of a cannon. A thin copper tube or a wooden frame would serve to launch them. And since they did not recoil, they could even be fired from small boats. (Strictly speaking, a rocket has its own recoil, too. But this goes into the exhaust gases, not into a barrel and breech.) They could be aimed about as closely as big guns and were far less expensive. The British government adopted them to good effect. During the Napoleonic Wars, naval rocket bombardment started disastrous fires in the cities of Boulogne, Copenhagen, and Danzig. The army rocket corps also distinguished itself.

The use of the weapon was not always successful. An intense attack failed to reduce the American Fort McHenry in 1814. The sight of his country's flag still flying at dawn above the walls inspired Francis Scott Key to write what has become our national anthem. His line, "the rockets' red glare," refers to Congreve missiles.

The military rocket almost disappeared before 1900. The reason was the same as it had been in the Middle Ages. Guns improved until they were better for every warlike purpose.

Yet some men felt that the rocket need not only destroy lives and property. It could also save them. Around 1840, use of the rocket at sea was perfected. When a vessel runs aground, especially in a storm, it is often impossible for swimmers or lifeboats to get through the wild surf. But a rocket can carry a line from ship to shore, or vice versa. Then crew and passengers can ride a breeches buoy along the line to safety. We have already mentioned signals, particularly distress signals, as another valuable application of the rocket.

Other uses were suggested, too, such as carrying air mail, and some were even tried. In World War I, the French launched incendiary rockets from airplanes to shoot down German Zeppelins and the tethered balloons from which soldiers spotted targets for artillery. But by and large, the later nineteenth and earlier twentieth centuries saw little employment of reaction devices.

On the other hand, that was the period when they began to be seriously considered for space travel. Men in different countries had, for some time, speculated about rocket power for aircraft. They gradually realized that such a vehicle might be able to go where no other could reach, out across the immense emptiness between planets.

The first man who seems to have proposed this was the German inventor Hermann Ganswindt in about 1890. The date is not known for certain because he spoke about the subject long before he wrote anything down. His ideas are interesting. Among other things, he realized that a spaceship crew must have protection against violent accelerations as well as outer-space conditions. Unfortunately, he insisted that the motor not shoot out gas but solid steel balls. This is quite impractical.

The next pioneer was a Russian, Konstantin Eduardovitch Tsiolkovsky, who first published an article on space flight in 1895. He was far more thorough and accurate than Ganswindt, and devoted many years to studies of the problems involved. But his work was also neglected.

The space age did not begin with either of these men, however, but with two others. The American scientist Robert Goddard wrote a paper in 1919 called "A Method Reaching Extreme Altitudes." While he was mainly interested in rockets as a means of studying the upper atmosphere, he did suggest sending one to the moon. When it crash-landed, an explosive charge would make a bright flare that could be seen from Earth. The proposal attracted a good deal of attention at the time. Goddard spent most of his remaining life in work—not just theorizing, but experimenting—with long-range rockets; and his were the first to use liquid fuel.

Beginning in 1923, the Rumanian-German Hermann Oberth issued a really thorough mathematical treatment of the subject. Instead of speculating in vague general terms, Oberth developed the formulas for calculating what is necessary to do something with a practical spacecraft. For example, he showed what the energy requirements are for various possible undertakings such as a journey to the moon. His work is rightfully considered the cornerstone of astronautics. Another German, Walter Hohmann, made similar valuable contributions not long after. They included working out different orbits by which a ship could reach moon and planets. These men, and others like the Frenchman Robert Esnault-Pelterie, presently arrived at a basic conclusion. For space missions, the traditional solid fuels would not do. Liquid-fuel motors were required.

Hitherto, rockets had consisted essentially of some such material as gunpowder packed into a casing and ignited from behind. The stuff was not supposed to explode or to burn so slowly that nothing happened. Rather, its combustion produced hot gases. Streaming out the end, these gases pushed the rocket forward according to the third law of motion. This type of device is still common for signaling, rescue work, Fourth of July fireworks, and similar things. Naturally, its design was improved over the centuries. Better fuels were compounded, and they were loaded in so as to burn with high efficiency. Some included their own oxidizing substances, and therefore did not depend on the oxygen of the atmosphere.

But ordinary solid fuels are not energetic enough for astronautics. They do not produce a fire-stream so fast that the rocket can completely escape from Earth's gravitational grip. To give an example, let us look at the ideal exhaust velocity. This is the rate at which gases would come out of the rocket if everything worked perfectly, which it never does. It is around 10,000 feet per second for a typical compacted powder. Without going into the mathematics, we can say that this means a perfect rocket so powered must spend 39 pounds of fuel for every pound that it lifts clear into space.

In contrast, a mixture of hydrogen and oxygen might well attain an exhaust velocity of 16,400 feet per second. Only 8.5 pounds of fuel would be needed to liberate 1 pound of spaceship from our planet.

Even so, we can see that many tons are necessary to raise a vessel of any reasonable size. So much gas could not possibly be compressed into tanks. Instead, it must be cooled until it turns liquid. That temperature is approximately 300 degrees below zero Fahrenheit for oxygen, and a good deal lower for hydrogen. This fact leads to many problems.

Indeed, these problems are so severe that only recently has anyone had success with this exact combination. Most rockets still burn materials such as gasoline, kerosene, or alcohol. Liquid oxygen is often the oxidizer, that is, the substance that combines with the fuel to release energy. But others, like hydrogen peroxide, nitric acid, and chlorine, have also been used as oxidizers.

Solid-fuel rockets cannot be written off. Greatly improved versions are in use today, especially as military missiles. They can reach high speeds and cover long distances. No doubt they will play a role in space. But it seems unlikely that any will ever become as powerful as the best liquid-fuel vehicles.

The work of the pioneers in rocketry inspired people to form astronautical societies in many different countries during the 1920's. The members of these groups were mostly enthusiastic amateurs, but some were professional scientists and engineers.

The clubs devoted themselves to furthering the cause of space travel. They held meetings, corresponded with their fellow associations, arranged lectures, published magazines and books, and sometimes did their own research.

The most active society was the German. It included several experts and built a number of machines that tested out promisingly. But in 1933, the evil government of Adolf Hitler and his Nazi party took power in Germany. Before long, those rocketeers who had not fled their country were put to work on weapons for war.

During World War II, rockets became important again. Every major power used them. For instance, the Americans had their bazooka, which launched a small missile from a tube. Because both ends of this tube were open, the recoil did not push against the soldier who was using the weapon. So he could shoot a much larger explosive charge than would otherwise have been possible. Another prominent weapon was the Russian Katyusha ("Sweet Little Catherine"), which sent a whole barrage off at once. Numerous others were also employed, generally against aircraft or tanks.

These were all solid-fuel missiles. They have the advantage of being far more storable and portable than liquid-fuel devices, which require elaborate refrigeration and pumping. But the most famous and important rocket of World War II was liquid-fueled, the German V-2.

The letter V stood for *Vergeltungswaffe,* "Revenge Weapon," and was supposed to signify retaliation for Allied bombings. The first of the series, V-1, was not a rocket but a kind of unmanned jet plane, an aerial torpedo, carrying about a ton of high explosive. Although the thousands that were fired caused much death and destruction, the British and Americans soon learned methods of intercepting them.

The V-2 missile was another matter. A 46-foot rocket, weigh-

ing 14 tons when fully fueled with alcohol and liquid oxygen, it carried the same payload as V-1. But because it could reach speeds up to a mile a second or better, there was no way at the time to stop it and the English suffered terribly from the 1,050 V-2's that struck their country.

The Germans and Japanese developed several other effective reaction weapons, including a fighter plane. But these did not overbalance Allied strength, and in 1945 Germany and Japan surrendered.

Of the victorious nations, the United States and the Soviet Union were particularly interested in missiles. Both took home as much German material and hired as many German specialists as possible. Both countries had native experts, too, and soon trained more. These are not the only powers that have made progress in rocketry since the war. So have Britain, France, and Japan. But the American and Soviet efforts have been the largest, with the most spectacular results. Much of this, unhappily, has been because of military rivalry. But much has also been for peaceful purposes.

What was perhaps the first true space flight occurred in February 1949. That was when a two-stage rocket went up from the American testing grounds at White Sands, New Mexico.

There is a reason for a rocket having more than one stage. Even a perfect vehicle with energetic fuel must consume a great deal to get aloft. Air friction, inefficiency, and other factors raise this price. It may be too large to pay. That is, if we want to put, say, one ton into orbit, we may not be able to build a machine big enough to do the job alone. But suppose we know how to make one which can lift five tons part of the way. By the time

A V-2 rocket rises faster than sound to an altitude of seventy-five miles above the White Sands testing grounds in New Mexico.

its fuel is gone, it is above the worst air resistance. Earth's gravity is also a little weaker at that altitude. Now suppose this first stage, or booster, releases its payload—which is another, smaller rocket. Having ridden "piggyback" so far, gaining not only height but velocity, the second one can spend its own fuel more effectively. This may serve to complete the mission.

In reality, matters are more complicated than that. But the idea of two or more stages is fundamental to present-day astronautics, and will remain so for a long time to come.

On that day in 1949, at White Sands a modified V-2 lifted another of the "WAC Corporal" type. When the second stage blasted free, it got to 250 miles above sea level. Then it crashed. But for all practical purposes, it had entered space. The stars, frost-cold and unwinking in that near-vacuum, had looked upon the work of humans in flight.

CHAPTER

3

Man-made Moons

A generation after V-2, rockets have developed fantastically in size, power, and capability. There are too many kinds, serving too many different purposes, for us to list here. But three American models are among the most reliable big vehicles today, the work horses of our space program.

Atlas: Length, 82.5 feet. Diameter, 16 feet at the base, 10 feet at the tanks. Weight, 260,000 pounds. Range when used as a missile, 9,000 miles. Among other things, it was the first-stage booster for Project Mercury, the beginning of manned spaceflight in our country. It has frequently been used with an Agena rocket for the second stage; the combination stands 98 feet tall.

Thor Agena: Length, 81 feet. Maximum diameter, 8 feet. Weight, 123,000 pounds. This two-stager can put 1,600 pounds into orbit 300 miles above Earth. The Agena B has a motor that can be stopped and restarted on radio command. This is critically important for reaching the moon.

Titan 2: Length, first stage, 70 feet; second stage 32, for a

A Mercury spacecraft stands atop an Atlas launch vehicle. Piloted by Astronaut L. Gordon Cooper, the craft was scheduled for twenty-two orbits.

total of 102 feet. Diameter, 10 feet. Weight, 300,000 pounds. Its motors develop a total thrust of more than 500,000 pounds. It was the booster for Project Gemini.

There are vehicles that dwarf even these. But the existing machines are certainly awesome. So is the sight of one blasting off. Movies and television have made it familiar: the countdown, the tension in the blockhouse as zero approaches, the gantry crane withdrawing from the launching pad, the vapors streaming down the fuel-chilled flanks of the giant—and then the thunder, the flame, and the burning spear hurled skyward!

Perhaps we have gotten too used to the spectacle. It has become hard for us to appreciate what an achievement every flight really is.

To understand this, let us examine not the construction of a major rocket, which would take many books to describe, but a few of the problems.

The principle of the rocket motor is deceptively simple. Fuel and oxidizer are pumped from their separate tanks into a combustion chamber. Here they combine in fire, turning into gases that move at high speeds because of the released energy. These gases flow out through a nozzle whose narrow-throated shape is designed to get the maximum work from them. Reaction pushes the rocket as a whole forward.

One can immediately guess some of the difficulties. How is ultra-cold liquid oxygen to mix and burn satisfactorily with the fuel? How are the combustion chamber and rocket nozzle to withstand immense pressures and temperatures hotter than a welding torch? One answer to both questions is to circulate the liquid around the chamber before feeding it in, thereby warming it somewhat while it cools and reinforces the walls. In spite of this, pumps and fuel injectors must be extremely rugged as well as precise mechanisms; and the search goes on for materials that are more durable than what are now used.

The first joint American-Canadian launching used the Thor Agena vehicle with a Canadian satellite. This was the first Thor-Agena B launch vehicle configuration.

A Titan 2 rocket leaves the launching pad at Cape Kennedy. This 1966 attempt carried Astronauts James Lovell and Edwin Aldrin, in the Gemini 12 capsule, toward an orbit around Earth.

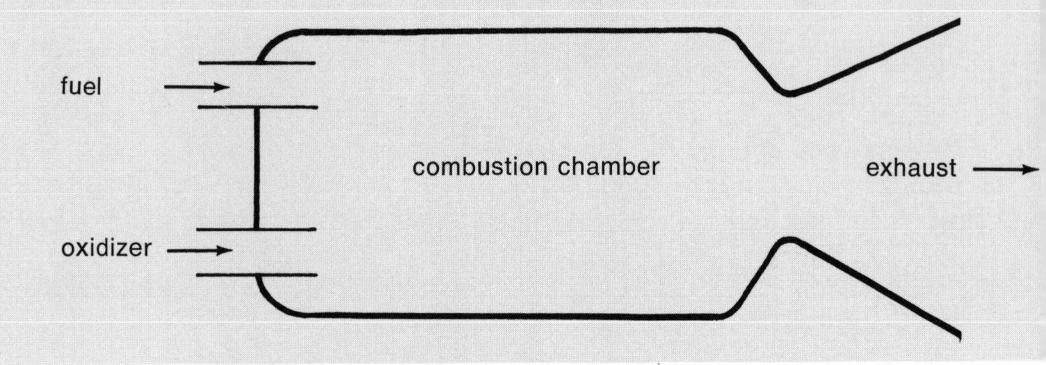

A liquid-fueled rocket motor: fuel and oxidizer are pumped from their separate tanks into a combustion chamber. Here they combine in fire, turning into gases that move at high speeds because of the released energy. These gases flow out, and reaction pushes the rocket forward.

The vehicle (outer shell, tanks, motors, and other hardware) must be as light as possible, so that fuel is not wasted in moving needless weight. Yet it must not give way under tons of thrust and acceleration pressure. Here again, space flight demands new alloys and compounds as well as high engineering skill.

This massive, towering machine is supposed to rise balanced on a mere jet. A strong gust of wind can upset it in flight, with disastrous results. That is one reason launchings are only made in good weather. But no matter how calm the air, the rocket is in a precarious situation. Furthermore, it is seldom sent straight up all the way. After gaining sufficient altitude, it is tilted in the direction that will take it where it is bound. And it does not even have a guide stick like a piece of fireworks. Controlling it involves gyroscopes, vanes in the rocket blast, side jets, swivel mountings, or other complicated systems. The least flaw anywhere along the line can bring the whole proud giant down in ruin.

Control poses an entire new set of problems. First, we have

to know exactly where our rocket is at any given instant. A worldwide network of radio tracking stations is necessary. Second, we often have to decide almost instantly what to make it do next. Is it headed into the planned orbit? If not, how much thrust, for how long, in what direction, do we need to get on course? Questions like these cannot be answered fast enough by living brains. The space age would be impossible without computers that make the calculations in millionths of a second. Third, we must transmit the command through all the interference of atmosphere and space. Fourth, the rocket must respond properly —which brings us back to its own intricate structure.

We should not wonder at occasional failures. The marvel is that the big birds fly as well as they do, after so short a period of evolution as they have had thus far.

By 1957 rockets were sufficiently well developed that both the United States and the Soviet governments announced their intention of placing artificial satellites in orbit around Earth. This was in connection with the International Geophysical Year, when most countries were working together in a special effort to study our planet. Satellites would give information that could be gotten in no other way.

To see why that is so, we must return to Newton: this time, to his law of gravitation. It states that every body in the universe attracts every other body with a force that is proportional to its mass and inversely proportional to the square of the distance between the two. That sounds more formidable than it is. The law is not really hard to understand.

Suppose we have two bodies. They might be stars or planets, they might be mere atoms, or anything else. It makes no difference. Let us call them A and B. If you are equally far from them both, but A has twice the mass of B, then A pulls on you with just twice the force that B does. One thousand times the mass means one thousand times the gravitational pull, and so on for any and all masses. That is what we mean in saying that the force of attraction that a body exerts is proportional to its mass.

Now imagine that A and B have the same mass, but B is twice as far away from you as A is. For instance, B might be two miles distant, A only one. The square of a number is that number multiplied by itself; so the square of B's two-unit distance is four squared units. The inverse of a number is simply the fraction one divided by that number. So the inverse of four, which is the inverse square of two, is just one-fourth. Therefore B, twice as distant as A, pulls you only one-fourth as hard as A does. If B were three times as distant, it would attract with one-ninth the force of A; four times as distant, and the pull is one-sixteenth; and so on.

You attract A and B in your turn. Indeed, you attract everything in the universe. But most objects are too big, like the Earth, or too far away, like atoms in interstellar space, or too energetic, like air molecules, for this to have any effect that we can measure.

It is almost, though not quite, true that a large body pulls as if its mass were concentrated in one point at the center. That is, standing on the surface of Earth, you are about 4,000 miles from its center. If you went 4,000 miles straight up, you would be 8,000 miles from the midpoint, twice as far as at sea level. Accordingly, Earth's tug on you would have dropped to one-fourth of the value you are used to. At the distance of the moon, it has only about one thirty-six-hundredth of its sea-level strength.

Nonetheless, that force keeps the moon accompanying us. From this we can see that, strictly speaking, there is no such thing as escaping from any planet's gravity. It reaches out to the ends of creation. But naturally, at a large distance it is very weak. As we approach another body like the moon, its tug becomes much the strongest upon us. At last, when we are quite near, this particular gravitational attraction is the only one we need reckon with.

If we throw a ball or shoot a bullet straight upward, it rises a certain distance before falling down again. The faster it starts off, the higher it goes. As it rises, Earth's gravity acts on it, accelerating it downward. (Remember that an acceleration is any change of velocity, including a slowing.) So it moves less and less rapidly. When the last upward velocity is gone, it begins to fall.

If we gave it a suitable speed, it could rise for thousands of miles. At those heights, thanks to the inverse square law, the downward acceleration is less. The object might have more velocity left than Earth's drag could steal. In that case, it would keep on going. At the cost of some of its original momentum, it would be free of our planet.

The velocity that will just accomplish this is called escape velocity. For Earth, it is nearly 7 miles per second, or 25,200 miles per hour. Jules Verne's passenger-carrying shell had to leave the muzzle of the cannon at least this fast; in practice, air resistance raises the figure by quite a bit. As we have remarked, that kind of acceleration would have squashed anyone flat.

A rocket can lift in a less terrifying fashion, because its motors give a continuous push. But in the end, one way or another, quickly or leisurely, a spaceship bound for new worlds must gain that total 7 miles a second, plus whatever it needs to cross the gulf between planets in a reasonable time.

Escape velocity is less for smaller bodies. The moon's is only 1.5 miles a second, Mars's 3.1. But for huge Jupiter the value is 39.

One might ask at this point, "If gravitation draws everything together, why doesn't the moon fall onto Earth, Earth into the sun, the whole universe into a lump?" The answer brings us, at last, to satellites and their orbits.

Imagine that you are standing on a hilltop on an otherwise perfectly round Earth and that there's no air to resist motion. Now imagine that you shoot bullets from a gun held parallel to the ground below. You would see them curve downward, drawn by gravity. But the bigger your powder charge, the faster they would travel and the farther they would go before plowing into the soil. After all, the acceleration of gravity takes a while to bring anything downward; and in that time a rapid bullet will cover a long distance. Eventually, you would find a speed at which the bullet never touches the ground. Earth's surface curves away beneath it as fast as gravity curves its path downward, so to speak. Without air friction, the bullet would then go around and around the world forever—if you got out of its way! It would be in orbit.

Another way of thinking about orbits is to remember what it is like to whirl a weight around your head at the end of a piece

Bullets shot from a gun held parallel to a perfectly smooth Earth will curve downward because of the pull of gravity. By increasing the powder charge, a speed can be reached at which the bullet will never touch the ground: it will be in orbit.

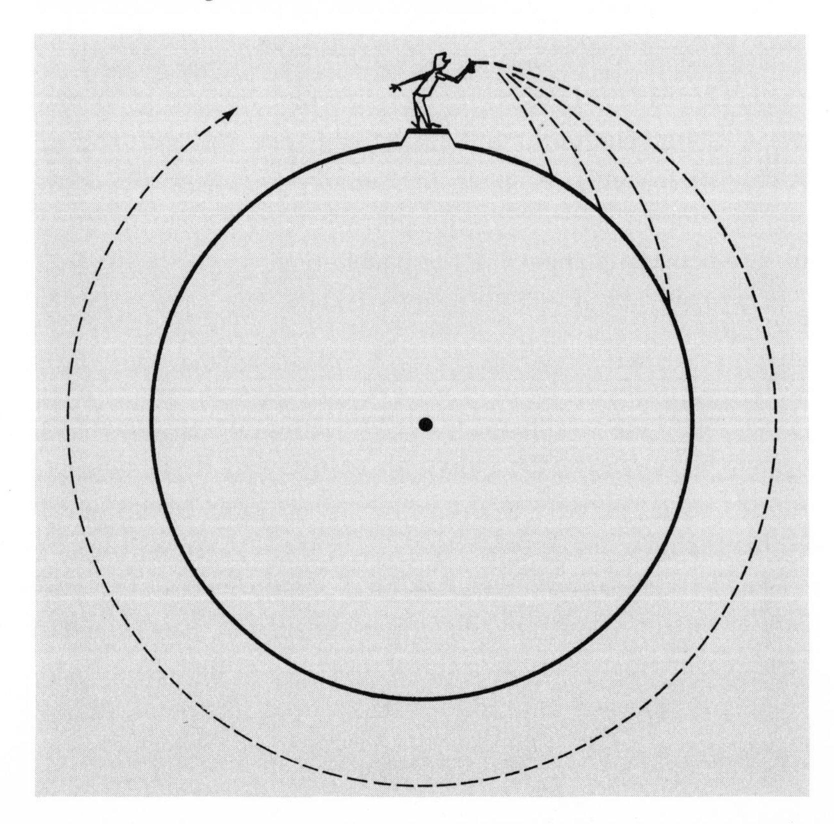

of string. The string is drawn taut; you can feel the weight tugging outward. Newton's laws explain what is happening. If you were to let go, the weight would fly off in a straight line, as nearly as possible (first law). But since its direction of movement is, instead, continuously changing, it is being accelerated by a force that you exert through the string (second law). This action has a reaction, in the so-called centrifugal force that makes the weight pull on your arm (third law).

A planet in orbit around the sun, or a satellite in orbit around a planet, behaves similarly. Gravity accelerates it inward, centrifugal force outward. When these two balance, the orbiting body moves in a closed curve. To do this, it must have such a speed that centrifugal force does just equal gravity where it is. That speed is known as orbital velocity. (We say "velocity" because it does have a definite direction, even though this is constantly changing.) In the neighborhood of Earth, its value is five miles per second. Further out, where the gravity pull is weaker, orbital velocity is less. The moon trundles along at a mere two-thirds of a mile per second.

As Kepler discovered, orbits are seldom, if ever, circles. They are ellipses. This means that an orbiting body is sometimes closer to the one it is going around than at other times. When closer, it necessarily moves faster.

If it comes fairly near, the larger world no longer acts as if all the mass were at the center. Instead, those parts that are closer draw noticeably harder on the satellite than the farther parts. This causes peculiar shifts and wobbles in the orbit. By studying and mathematically analyzing that behavior, we can learn much about the exact shape, mass, and even composition of Earth.

This was one possibility that inspired the satellite launches in 1957.

Little attention had been paid in Western countries to the

Russian declarations. It came as a total surprise to most people when, on October 4, the Soviets orbited the first man-made moonlet. Astonishment and chagrin redoubled when this Sputnik (a word that simply means satellite in Russian) turned out to weigh almost 184 pounds, far bigger and heavier than anything the Americans could hope to lift for years to come.

Sputnik's altitude varied between 142 and 588 miles. Thus it passed through layers of the atmosphere that were not too thin to make it lose energy by friction. Slowed to less than orbital velocity, it lacked enough centrifugal force to balance gravity and had to spiral inward to a new, closer path. But that brought it still deeper into the air. This process, orbital decay, caused it to fall completely and burn up like a meteorite in three months.

It had not carried much aboard. In fact, besides position, the only information that that famous *beep-beep-beep* on its radio transmitter gave was the temperature inside. But from this, plus its motions, a considerable amount could be deduced.

The rocket which launched it was impressive, 105 feet high, 12.2 feet in diameter, 156,000 pounds in weight, a three-stager put together from existing parts for this one purpose.

With such a commanding lead, during the next several years the Russians were the first to do most things in space. The Americans came later. But gradually the United States began to catch up, and in some cases to surpass the Soviet achievements. Certainly the Americans have put more objects aloft, including instruments that are apparently more sensitive and reliable, and have accumulated more man-hours in space. It seems quite possible that there is no rocket mightier than the American Saturn.

Varied benefits have come from the hundreds of satellites which have been orbited to date. Besides purely scientific information, certain of them transmit views of Earth seen from space. These pictures are of invaluable help in improving our maps and weather forecasts. Communications satellites have brought

A photograph of Sputnik, mounted on a stand, taken by Russian photographers before the first man-made satellite was launched in 1957.

direct international television far sooner and cheaper than could have been done with Earthbound relays. Navigation satellites aid men to find where they are on the seas and in the skies.

Above all, satellites have been, and are, trailblazers for man in space. Through them, we have learned that our planet is girdled with a zone of trapped electrified particles. Radiation within this so-called Van Allen belt could be deadly to an unprotected astronaut; but now we have been warned. Likewise, we have learned about the lethal radiation that occasionally seethes from the sun. We eventually hope to predict such outbursts well in advance. Then, if the storm is going to be so bad that astronauts cannot find enough shelter inside their vessels, we can ground them until it is over.

Besides showing us what to look out for, satellites have calmed certain fears. Meteoroids are a case in point. Although mostly small, these bits of stone zip through space at speeds up to several miles per second. Once it was thought that they might riddle a ship and its crew like a blast from a cosmic machine gun. But we have learned that they are not really so numerous or so dangerous.

Experiments with animals and plants, orbited in unmanned satellites, are teaching us an immense amount about biology, and particularly about the effects of unearthly environment.

CHAPTER 4

Lunar Landing

The first man in orbit was a Russian. On April 12, 1961, Yuri Gagarin made one circuit around Earth and returned safely. The next was another Russian, Gherman Titov. On August 6 and 7, only four months after Gagarin's flight, Titov stayed in space for better than 25 hours, rounding our planet 17.5 times before he descended. Like all spacecraft from their country, they parachuted down onto land rather than into the ocean as American craft do.

The Soviet enterprise differs from ours in numerous other respects. Hitherto it has used more powerful boosters and has therefore been able to raise heavier payloads. That situation may now be changing. The Soviets have, as we already remarked, launched fewer objects of almost every type. But theirs is the honor of sending off the first spacemen . . . and also the world's only spacewoman, Valentina Tereshkova, in 1963. They may yet be first on the moon. But no one outside their government

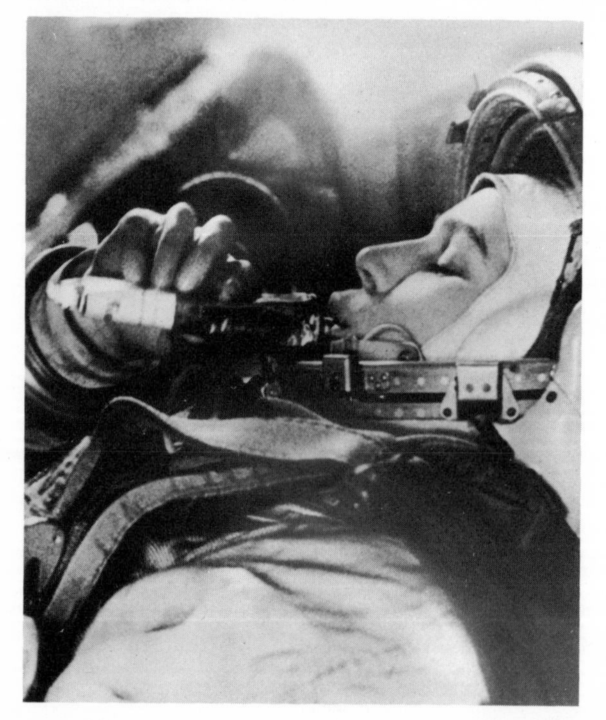

Three Russian cosmonauts: (above, left and right) Yuri Gagarin and Gherman Titov, the first men in space; (below) Valentina Tereshkova, the first woman in space.

knows if they seriously desire it. In contrast to the United States, the Soviet Union has no official goals set far in advance for its space program. The Russians do intend to explore the Solar System with both instruments and manned expeditions. But they seem to be going about it in a slower, more methodical fashion than we.

Both Russia and the United States had space programs under way when the first Sputnik was launched. These programs continued to grow. Among other undertakings, animals were put into orbit for various periods of time. Instruments radioed back the information that they stayed in reasonably good health. There was every reason to believe humans would survive, and both countries made ready for manned trips.

Three weeks after Gagarin's mission, the first American was sent aloft, Commander Alan Shepard, Jr. His assignment was not to duplicate the Russian feat but merely to test the system. This he did in a successful suborbital flight. From the great rocket base at what was then called Cape Canaveral (now Cape Kennedy), he rode his Mercury capsule 107 miles into the heavens and splashed smoothly down into the Atlantic, hard by a waiting recovery team.

Meanwhile President John F. Kennedy had asked Congress to establish a national goal of putting men on the moon before the end of the decade. The resolution passed with little dissent, and the United States was committed. Under the National Aeronautics and Space Administration, usually referred to as NASA, an already large endeavor now burgeoned enormously. It is concerned with much more than the lunar landing. Despite occasional setbacks, it has many brilliant accomplishments to its credit.

We have seen how intricate a big rocket is. Science fiction stories about some professor who builds a spaceship by himself and goes off to the planets are strictly fiction, not science. It takes years of work by thousands of men to produce a new kind of vehicle. Sometimes the knowledge necessary to design it must be gathered before the engineers can even start drawing up plans. And no matter how careful the designers are, they will likely find unforeseen flaws that can only be discovered and eliminated by tests.

This is especially true of a craft that is to carry a human being. What *are* the requirements? For billions of years, from its very beginning, earthly life has been nowhere but on Earth. Evolution has fitted us for this single planet. Space is utterly alien. How can anyone survive beyond the sky?

Obviously astronauts must take their own air along, and remain sealed in their ship or at least in their spacesuits during the whole trip. But matters are not that simple. A vessel in orbit is in a state of free fall; weight does not exist. Hence, air does not circulate automatically. A man could smother in his own exhaled breath, unable to get enough fresh oxygen. We can avoid that danger by forced ventilation. But what about the waste products that the body emits through lungs and skin? These are not only carbon dioxide and water vapor. They include small amounts of acetone, organic acids, and other compounds. Here at home, we have an atmosphere to sweep them away and a living world to consume them. But accumulating for weeks in a spacecraft, they would make it worse than stuffy and ill-smelling. They would make it deadly. Therefore, we must develop means to get rid of them, and that is not easy.

What should the spaceman's air be like? We know that it need not be at sea-level pressure, and a lower density saves weight. Still more weight can be saved if the air is pure oxygen. The Americans have used that method so far. But the tragic deaths of astronauts Virgil Grissom, our second Mercury pilot, Edward White, our first man to go outside an orbiting craft,

Astronaut Alan B. Shepard, Jr., is hoisted to safety by a hovering helicopter. In a successful suborbital flight, he rode his Mercury capsule 107 miles into the heavens.

and young Roger Chaffee, showed the fire hazard of such an atmosphere. That is doubtless one reason why the Russians have stayed with an ordinary mixture of nitrogen and oxygen. Their scientists also maintain that prolonged lack of nitrogen will damage the lungs.

Air is only one difficult area among many. The weightlessness of orbital flight is another. Is it harmful after more than a few seconds? To be sure, an astronaut can keep up his muscle tone with exercises. But what about digestion, circulation, and the nervous system? How dependent are they on a constant downward pull? Tests show that a man who has been in free fall reacts less quickly than normal. After a while, blood pools in the lower parts of the limbs, causing swelling and some difficulty in walking. Neither of these conditions has proved serious thus far, and nature has soon corrected them once the spacemen came home. But this was not known when missions were first planned. Titov created some alarm by reporting that he felt ill because of his day aloft. Apparently he was exceptional. Nearly everyone who came after him said weightlessness was pleasant. But that, again, could not have been predicted with certainty.

Temperature control was another problem that needed solving. Space has no breezes to carry away the sun's heat or to warm the chill of a shadow. Ordinary air conditioning is out of the question. We require better methods to keep the astronauts from roasting or freezing. These include paint patterns that absorb and reflect just enough of the unshielded solar glare.

Earth's atmosphere and magnetic field guard us from most cosmic radiation. A spaceship is naked to it. The walls give some protection, apparently sufficient except when the sun spits out a hurricane of charged particles. As yet, we have no really satisfactory way of coping with that menace.

These are but a few examples of the demands that we must

Left to right: Astronauts Roger Chaffee, Edward White, and Virgil Grissom seated inside their Apollo 1 spacecraft simulator.

meet. Furthermore, we must meet them within the size and weight limits that are set by the rockets available. Each system of ship and booster, each group of missions, has provided experience and information that were essential before the next step could be taken.

Therefore, our lunar enterprise has had three distinct stages—Projects Mercury, Gemini, and Apollo. The first two have been completed. The third will end with men on the moon.

The Mercury craft, or capsule, was small. It held one man, who stayed in his seat. So it did not have to be as heavy or elaborate as its successors. Naturally, it was far more than a box, being in fact extremely complex. And the men who rode those capsules were not mere passengers. They made vital observations, of the vehicle as it operated, of the space environment, of their own bodies adjusting to the strangeness. Like all spacemen everywhere, they set the world a bright example of courage, dedication, and intelligence.

The third Mercury astronaut was the first American to make a true space flight. On February 20, 1962, looking like a knight of old in his white spacesuit and helmet, John Glenn rode the elevator to his *Friendship 7* where it sat atop the huge Atlas booster. He settled down inside; the rocket motors roared and blazed; acceleration pressed him into his seat with brutal force. The time was not long before his capsule broke free and whirled off around Earth. Then, except for voices over the buzzing, crackling radio, he was alone.

That is an experience at once weird and heartlifting. You have no weight but float as if in a dream. The stars glitter wintry keen, untwinkling, against an endless black. Earth dominates, enormous, vaporous, largely a blue that becomes a lovely deep shade at the horizon, though some greens and browns show through. This close, the capsule goes once around our planet in an hour and a half. Each time dawn and nightfall are seen and a bluish-white sun that rises and sets in reds, golds, and oranges as its rays pierce the atmosphere. After dark, in Earth's shadow, you can make out lightning flashes among the clouds and the sparks that are cities. The moon gleams brilliant when it is visible; when it is not, Earth is darker than the sky.

Glenn made three complete orbits as planned. Then he fired his retrorockets. They pushed opposite to the capsule's velocity,

Astronaut John H. Glenn, Jr., stands beside the Mercury-Atlas spacecraft Friendship 7. *Glenn made three complete orbits around Earth in February, 1962.*

making it lose speed. Therefore, it fell inward, like Sputnik braked by the air, until it too entered the atmosphere. But it had protection against burning up, a heat shield. This turned white-hot and peeled away, layer by layer, under the fury of friction. But by so shedding energy, it slowed *Friendship 7* until parachutes could operate. They brought the vessel to a safe descent in the ocean, near the spot where Navy ships were waiting. That is the system that American spacecraft continue to use.

Scott Carpenter followed Glenn on a similar mission, then Walter Schirra on one twice as long. Finally, on May 16–17, 1963, Gordon Cooper's 34-hour, 22-circuit flight was so successful in every way that Project Mercury ended. It had done what it was supposed to do, and the stage was prepared for Project Gemini.

The Latin word means "twins," and refers in particular to the heavenly twins of classic myth, Castor and Pollux, for whom a constellation is also named. It was an appropriate name for a series of trips in which two men went spaceward together.

The Gemini capsule looked much like the Mercury except that, seen from the front, it appeared to have rather sad eyes. It was larger, however, and carried more equipment. In the two years of its project, a full dozen launchings took place, ten of them manned. Sometimes the astronauts failed to do as much as they had hoped. But this is hardly surprising when we think how ambitious their aims were. Altogether, they succeeded in everything essential.

The first manned Gemini flight lasted three orbits. It was chiefly to make sure the system was reliable. On the second such mission, Edward White left his companion James McDivitt behind and went outside the capsule at the end of a lifeline with no protection other than what he wore.

A Russian, Alexei A. Leonov, had managed a "space walk" three months earlier, from another two-man vehicle. He exited

Astronaut Edward White floats into space from the Gemini 4 spacecraft. He remained outside for twenty-one minutes before rejoining James A. McDivitt inside the ship.

through an airlock, that is, a double-door arrangement that prevents the air within the capsule from rushing into the cosmic vacuum. The Americans were still behind in development. Their Gemini had no corresponding facility. Instead, both men donned space gear and opened a hatch directly on the void.

Nevertheless, Americans have since performed a good deal more of this extra-vehicular activity or EVA than their Soviet colleagues. They have learned some surprising things, notably how hard it is. One would think that without weight, work should be easy. The only problem should be that tools are apt to drift away when laid aside. But in fact, EVA is exhausting. Probably the reason is that the body, unaccustomed to the lack of "up" and "down," strains needlessly and uses energy in fighting itself. Men who are to labor in orbit will need special training.

The Gemini series got valuable information on the effects of prolonged weightlessness. The Borman-Lovell flight lasted over 330 hours and neither man suffered harm. We do not yet know what might happen in a month or more. But at least it does not seem any problems will arise that cannot be solved.

In the course of Project Gemini, astronauts learned how to maneuver from one orbit to another. They learned how to rendezvous, that is, how to bring a space vehicle close to another vehicle or to an unmanned rocket already in orbit. They learned how to join their capsule to such an orbiting rocket, an operation known as docking. One partial failure was actually a kind of triumph. When a rocket misfired and threw two linked spacecraft into an ugly spin, Neil Armstrong and David Scott were forced to disengage and return home earlier than planned. But they *did* cope with the emergency.

In the Gemini series, the target for docking was an unmanned Agena rocket that had gone up beforehand. The astronauts eased the nose of their capsule into a collar on the Agena and locked it in place until they were ready to let go. The Conrad-Cooper Gemini 11 docked on the first orbit and used the restartable Agena engine to rise 850 miles above Earth. The Lovell-Aldrin Gemini 12, November 11–15, 1966, hooked up on the third orbit but then had fuel pump trouble. Undaunted, Charles Lovell got in a total of 5.5 hours of EVA, proving that the difficulties can be overcome. Since he had also been on the two-week Gemini 7 flight, he holds the present record for time in space, 425 hours, almost 18 whole days.

And that was the end of Gemini. Apollo, the final stage, has begun.

To send only three men to the moon will be an achievement that beggars the Pyramids. Among other things, it requires nearly inconceivable lifting power. So gigantic a booster could not even be designed in one step. No one knew how. Instead, the world's mightiest rocket (if the Russians are not preparing another surprise) was built mainly to gain experience. This was the Saturn 1 prototype. Since it tested out well, others may be made for various uses. But it is too little for Apollo. Now we have the moon rocket itself, Saturn 5.

The very building that protects Saturn 5 from the weather is incredible, the largest on this planet, so big that, without special air conditioning, clouds could form and rain could fall inside. When carrying the moonship, the assembly stands 387 feet tall, overtopping the Statue of Liberty. It weighs 6 million pounds. And, although the five engines of its first stage put out 7.6 million pounds of thrust—sufficient to orbit at once every American space vehicle that went before it—the engines get the spacecraft to an altitude of no more than 38 miles and a speed of under 2 miles per second.

At that point, the first stage drops off and the second ignites. In its 6.5 minutes of active life, this next quintet of motors

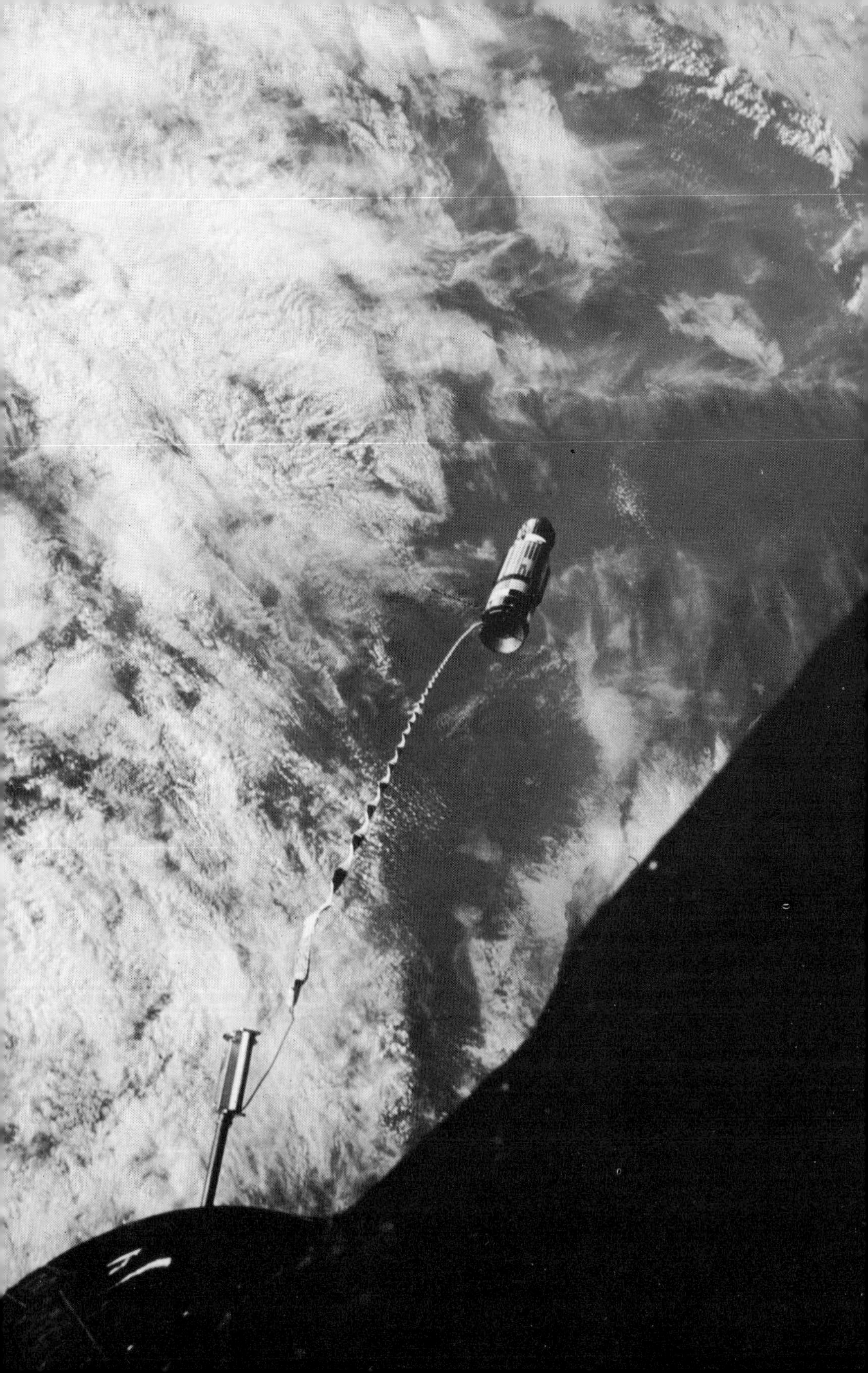

reaches a little over 4 miles a second. Then their stage is likewise discarded. The third goes on to enter Earth orbit. In the unmanned test flight of November 9, 1967, this orbit was 115 miles high. Later the single oxygen-hydrogen engine of the third stage restarted on radio command and attained an altitude of 11,400 miles.

There the Apollo vehicle that it was carrying separated from it and returned to Earth. Reentry took place at the same speed as the lunar astronauts will have, the same as escape velocity, 7 miles a second. The heat shield reached a temperature of some 4,500 degrees. But men would have survived. The test became a victory.

If all continues to go this well, then, perhaps as early as 1969, three men will be on their way to the moon.

If that is a lucky number, the omens are good. For three trios are involved. Besides the men, we have the three stages of the Saturn 5 booster and the three units, or modules, that will actually make the voyage.

From top to bottom as they sit on their rocket, the command module where the crew will live is first. From the outside it looks somewhat like a television picture tube. Its base is about 13 feet across, its maximum height about 12, its weight about 5 tons. Although cramped, it should not be too uncomfortable. Spacesuits need not be worn aboard. An airlock will allow the men to go in and out without emptying their cabin of atmosphere.

Below is the service module, a cylindrical rocket. It has the same 13-foot diameter but is about 23 feet long and weighs about 25 tons.

The Agena target docking vehicle is tethered to the Gemini 12 spacecraft. Crew members for this last flight in the Gemini program were Astronauts Lovell and Aldrin.

After two and a half minutes the first stage of Saturn 5 will drop off and the second stage ignite.

Finally, we have the lunar excursion module, familiarly called the LEM or, from its appearance, the "bug." This is the sixteen-ton, two-man capsule whose four shock-absorbing legs will touch upon the moon's surface.

To briefly describe the climax of Apollo: the first two stages of Saturn fire and drop off. The escape tower, a life-saving device in case of trouble, is then discarded. The third stage enters Earth orbit with three modules. At the right time, it fires again and is jettisoned. The linked-together modules are moonbound.

They do not use fuel to cross the nearly quarter million miles. The velocity that Saturn gave them, and the gravities of Earth, moon, and sun, determine an orbit. After a little less than three days, this course brings the astronauts toward their goal. During that time, they are weightless. But Mercury and Gemini have demonstrated that it will not hurt them.

The second stage will burn six and a half minutes before being discarded. The third stage will achieve Earth orbit.

Close to the moon, rocket power in the service module turns the whole train end for end, making it travel "backward." Now a blast slows down the craft until it enters an orbit around the moon. The altitude is roughly one hundred miles. At that distance, with no atmosphere to blur them, the great craters, desolate plains, and fanglike mountain peaks stand forth terrifyingly clear.

The landing follows.

First, the LEM detaches from the other modules, on radio signal. Next these others, which remain joined, turn around again through a half circle. That maneuver brings the command module nose-to-nose with the LEM. They dock. Two astronauts go through the connecting hatches, into the bug. This is one reason Project Gemini had to develop rendezvous and docking techniques.

Leaving their companion behind, the pair of men free the LEM. They fire its retrorockets and fall out of orbit toward the lunar surface. As they near that stony kingdom, they use the landing system to brake their speed and make an easy descent. The unmanned Surveyor craft have already shown that this can be done, as well as showing that the ground will bear the weight and not crumble under impact.

At this writing, the time of lunar day for the landing has not been decided. At night there is no danger from solar radiation, and Earth's bulk gives some shielding from meteoroids whizzing in toward the sun. The extreme cold will not be too severe a problem. But the darkness may well be. Although Earth, at lunar midnight, gives seventy times the light that the full moon does for us, this is not really much. And it falls on a murky, cindery surface, with no air or floating dust to scatter it around. A man standing there would seem to be under a dim bluish spotlight, and beyond it see a vast gloom. His flashlight could only throw another puddle of dull glow.

Besides heat, two hundred degrees Fahrenheit or worse, and possible lethal emissions, the sun at lunar midday has a searing brilliance. Furthermore, a pilot coming down would have trouble judging terrain without long shadows to pick out its uneven places for him.

Altogether, at present the best time for the LEM to arrive seems to be shortly before sunset. The moon rotates slowly, taking as long to do so as it does to go around Earth. Therefore, it always turns the same face to its companion, and the time from dawn to dawn is a full month. The astronauts need have no fear of being caught by sudden night.

Their stay lasts only some 18 hours, with 6 allotted for sleep and 6 more for checking their vehicle. In the remaining while, divided into two 3-hour periods, they venture forth afoot, one man at a time while the other stands by in the LEM. They

The LEM will land on the moon. Later, the lower stage will be the launching pad for the little rocket that will rendezvous with the orbiting command module.

radio descriptions and pictures of what they see back to Earth; they collect samples; they plant instruments that will continue to send information for a year after they have departed. All too soon, they embark for the return journey.

The lower stage of the LEM is their launching pad, left behind, no doubt to become a memorial for thousands of years. The rest of the ungainly little rocket makes rendezvous with the orbiting command module. The astronaut who has remained in space helps guide it to docking. After his friends have joined him inboard, the LEM is jettisoned. It continues to circle the moon, another ageless monument. The service module fires, putting the astronauts into a homeward orbit.

Near Earth, the last power in the service module goes to make whatever course corrections are necessary. Then it, too, is abandoned. Alone, at seven miles per second, the command module streaks into our sky. Air friction makes the heat shield incandescent but also slows the vessel. At last, parachutes can open and bring it down to the ocean. There the pick-up ships are waiting to receive the voyagers. And so is all mankind.

In those eight days, from launch to reentry, men have reached and walked upon another world.

Many people ask, "Why?" It will be a wonderful adventure, something to make our country remembered in history—but is it really worth the cost? Should billions upon billions of dollars, untold labor and ingenuity, be spent to let a pair of men experience less than one day on the moon?

The answer is, "Certainly not. But that is just the beginning."

Although instruments can tell us much, they can never do something for which they are not designed. For example, a magnetometer can inform us that the moon has little or no magnetic field. But it cannot report if the rocks are layered in strata like the rocks of Earth. It cannot see something odd and unexpected and go over for a close look. Man has only one instrument for discovering what is completely new, and that is man himself.

Granted, two astronauts in a few hours cannot begin to explore the multiple mysteries of an entire globe. And what about Mars, Venus, Jupiter, far Pluto, and even the stars?

We need men in our universe if we are ever to understand it. Among other things, this demands greatly improved spacecraft. That does not necessarily mean bigger rockets than Saturn. It does mean better ones, eventually atomic-powered. And it means bases in orbit and on other planets—actual colonies—so that expeditions no longer have to fight their way up from Earth.

At present, we must sadly admit that no such effort is under way in America. For lack of funds, NASA has no important plans beyond Apollo. It will continue to launch satellites and probes. It hopes to put an unmanned capsule or two on Mars in 1975 that will send back data. But it is not organizing further lunar landings or any human expeditions to our sister planets. We have seen how long a "lead time" is required for planning, designing, testing, and perfecting equipment. If we want to go on exploring space, the time to prepare is *now*. Otherwise, the effort that went into Apollo will be wasted indeed.

Meanwhile, the Soviet Union goes ahead, with less fanfare than us, and perhaps less capability, but with great earnestness. Russian books discuss man's future in space. In that nation, nothing is published unless the government approves. We will be wise to believe that the authors of those books mean what they say.

We do not want a bitter international rivalry. It is far better if people cooperate. Nevertheless, no matter how friendly, the nations that decide what is to be done in space are going to be the ones that are out there doing it. Surely the United States deserves a voice. This generation of Americans will determine the future of their country, in the Solar System as well as on Earth.

CHAPTER 5

MOL and Others

Since the Sputnik 1 launching, much has happened in the space close around us. The United States has put up by far the largest number of objects, but the Soviet Union has been busy, too, and now other countries such as France are joining in. Local activity is bound to increase. Its rewards are obvious, large, and quick to be paid.

There will be improved communications. More and better relay satellites are a certainty. Several orbits will be synchronous. This has already been achieved. A synchronous orbit is one at an altitude of 22,300 miles, where the time to go around Earth is 24 hours. In effect, a body there remains stationary above some chosen spot on the ground, which makes it especially useful for communications. Actually, unless it is precisely above the equator, and in a precisely circular orbit, it will seem to move back and forth along a short line. And the uneven pull of the planet makes the orbit wobble. But these are not serious drawbacks.

The military services maintain satellites for surveillance purposes. Carrying sensitive instruments, they send back a vast amount of information about what is occurring on the ground and the seas. Thus do the nations keep a wary eye on each other. Satellites may perhaps help to end that suspicion. To name one possible influence, the United States keeps some aloft to watch out for atomic explosions in space, which are forbidden by a treaty that most governments have signed. This reduces the temptation to break that treaty by conducting secret tests.

Spies in the sky raise the question of space law. Traditionally, a country controls its own air, and no foreign craft may pass above without permission. But how far up does that sovereignty extend? Could the passage of any satellite or spacecraft whatsoever be a violation? The point has not been formally settled. But as no one has made strong objections to astronautical projects, a new tradition seems to be developing by unspoken consent, that space is free to everyone like the high seas. Furthermore, the powers have renounced special claims to celestial bodies. No country is to seize the moon or another planet for its own. An agreement has lately been concluded that governments will help any foreign astronaut or cosmonaut forced down in their territories and return him home.

So, while no real body of space law exists as yet, and while military undertakings will no doubt continue for a long time, man in the cosmos is behaving better than he does on Earth. That alone could, in the end, justify everything we do out yonder.

The study of our globe has great value in itself. Weather satellites will grow in number and capability. Using their data, we will make increasingly accurate forecasts. In time, we will probably come to understand the atmosphere so well that we can modify the weather for human benefit.

That will require knowledge of the surrounding space, too. Studies are progressing satisfactorily. The most recent successes have been with a set of American satellites called Orbiting Geophysical Observatories, or OGO's for short. An OGO weighs

An artist's conception of the OGO in orbit around Earth. Experiments aboard the OGO have been designed to study the relationship between the sun and Earth's environment.

about 1,000 pounds. It carries the means for performing some 20 different kinds of experiments, investigating things like energetic particles, interplanetary dust and meteoroids, atmospheric conditions, and changes in the local magnetic field. Certain instruments are mounted on booms to get them away from the interference of the main body. With these booms extended, an OGO is 59 feet long. Although there have been some problems with it, we have already gained considerable information and can expect more. Before long, improved versions of the OGO will be ready.

Astronomy is another science that has profited from the space era. Earth's misty, dusty, turbulent air cuts down the light and distorts the images that reach a ground-based telescope or spectroscope. Worse, it blocks most kinds of radiation altogether. Not until instruments went above it in rockets did we really begin to learn about such features of the stars as the X-rays that they give off. These findings have upset many ideas and shown us phenomena whose very existence had never been suspected—for example, the radiation from certain clouds of interstellar gas.

Besides our desire to know the universe better, we have practical reasons for supporting astronomy. The stars and galaxies are like gigantic laboratories, where events take place that we midgets can never hope to duplicate. In studying them, we make discoveries about matter and energy that will enable us to carry out projects now impossible.

On this account, NASA has begun a series of Orbiting Astronomical Observatories. The first two-ton, seven-telescope OAO proved a disappointment when its power supply failed, but later models should correct that. Another, intended for solar research, performs well.

Power for these satellites, and for the probes that go into deep space, comes from various sources. Which one we use in a particular case depends on which is best for that particular system. Besides conventional electric batteries, there are fuel cells that produce electricity directly from a chemical reaction; thermistors that generate current from heat; and several kinds of solar cell that convert sunlight. In addition, early trials of small nuclear reactors to furnish atomic power in space have given encouraging results.

Since we are living beings ourselves, most of us care especially about life in space. Certainly we must know more than we do before we send men off on really extended missions. Many tests, such as those which study radiation dangers, are possible on Earth. But we can only produce weightlessness for a minute or so at a time, when an airplane makes an outside loop. To observe its effects over a long period, we must go into orbit.

Everyone today knows that astronauts can float inside or alongside their orbiting capsules. Many people, though, are still confused as to why. We observed in an earlier chapter that Earth's gravity field never comes to a definite end. At ordinary satellite altitudes, it is little weaker than at the surface. How, then, can a spaceman be without weight?

To understand this, imagine yourself riding an elevator, an old-fashioned one that does not operate smoothly. Starting upward, you feel a bit heavier than usual. The pressure of acceleration is added to the normal tug of gravity. But starting down, you feel a bit lighter. Now the acceleration is in the opposite direction. The corresponding force (second law) is subtracted from the force of gravity instead of added to it.

Suppose the cable broke and the elevator fell down the shaft. Or, to take a less alarming illustration, suppose you were in an airplane whose pilot cut off the engines briefly for a prank. In either case, you are now inside a falling object. Until air resistance begins to slow it, the floor will approach the ground with the same acceleration as you. Everything is still in the clutch of Earth's gravity. But you no longer have anything solid beneath your feet.

When you stand on a firm surface, you are drawn downward with a force that is proportional to your mass. Obeying the third law, the surface exerts an equal force on you. But if the surface is not firm, if you and it are falling at the same rate, how can you press on it and it press back? Weight *is* this force. When you are in free fall—that is, falling with nothing to resist you—you no longer have weight, though your mass is unchanged.

(The third law continues to hold good. Earth pulls you and you pull Earth, through gravity. But the force that, each second, makes you travel thirty-two feet per second faster, does not budge the mass of a planet enough to measure.)

Harking back to our imaginary bullet fired around the world, we can see that a body in orbit is also falling freely. If it is something like the moon, it draws objects to itself by its own gravity. But a spaceship has so small a mass that its attraction is not noticeable. With the vehicle and himself tumbling together at the same rate around Earth—or around the sun on a longer trip—an astronaut has no weight. This condition is often called zero gravity. That is a misnomer, since gravity is still present. But the phrase is so well established that we will probably never get rid of it.

Besides the astronaut, all his equipment and supplies are weightless in orbit. Things hang where they were left, except when air currents, rotation, or the like make them bob about. The least force accelerates them, on which account space-walking men have watched some fairly valuable gear soar away out of reach. Water does not pour, and does not lie quietly in a container. It forms globules, like mercury, that likewise float. This means our astronaut cannot drink from a cup, but must suck liquid from a bottle with a nipple. It also makes personal cleanliness difficult, though not impossible. Foods must not only be concentrated to save weight (Earthside weight, constant mass) but should not produce crumbs.

The nuisances seem endless. Many can be eliminated. For instance, anything that has iron in it, even a thin coating of iron, will cling to a magnetized surface. Glue, tape, hooks, tethers, clips, and so on will secure objects. Although, as we have seen, a man needs special skills to do physical labor in free fall without exhausting himself, it should be feasible to develop a training program.

But what does weightlessness do to the body?

We know that lack of exercise has evil results. The voluntary muscles shrink and soften. And so do the heart and bones. Digestion and circulation grow sluggish. This causes nerves and brain to work less well than they should. Without so much as the normal effort of supporting himself against gravity, a man will rapidly become an invalid. To be sure, he can do exercises, even in a cramped space vehicle. This is how the astronauts keep fit on their missions.

But might there be subtler consequences of weightlessness? Are there effects that creep forward too slowly to show up in weeks, but that would be crippling or fatal in the course of months?

And then we can imagine other factors that might be important in the long haul, such as radiation, atmospheric electricity, magnetism, and sheer monotony. Perhaps these are all hobgoblins that will never make trouble. But we have to find out beforehand. And, if we discover real dangers, we must develop means to cope with them.

For these reasons, as well as for basic research, numerous

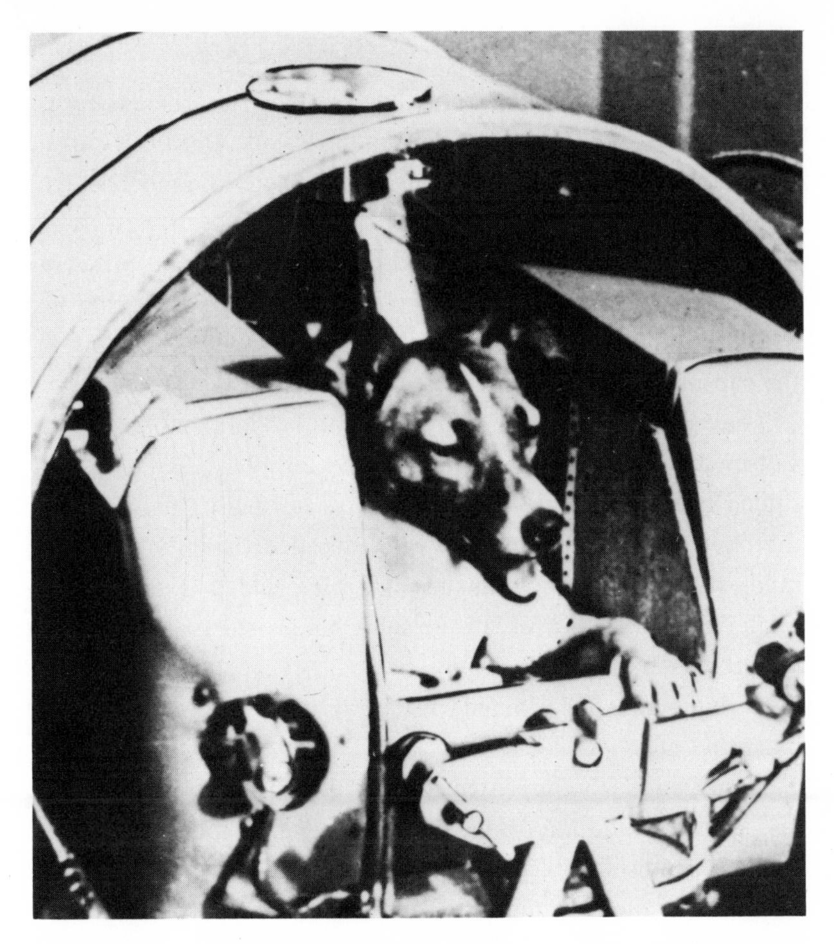

Laika, the world's first space traveler, was photographed in an air conditioned cabin before she was rocketed into space aboard Sputnik 2.

living organisms have been shot into space over the years. The most famous no doubt is the Russian dog Laika. But the most useful thus far belong to humbler species with which the Americans have been experimenting.

For example, on September 7, 1967, workers at Cape Kennedy sent up the capsule designated Biosatellite 2. After it had spent about forty-five hours in orbit, they fired its retrorockets by remote control and it was recovered in the Pacific Ocean. It carried a variety of small living things, including bacteria, amoebae, frog eggs, gnats, wasps, pepper plants, and wheat seedlings. While still aloft, from time to time its mechanisms killed and preserved sample specimens. This enabled the scientists to check what had happened hour by hour, as well as the final results after they got the capsule back.

The data are still under study, and a full report is not available. But evidently some astonishing things took place. Bacteria multiplied twenty or thirty times as fast as normally. This suggests that weightlessness affects the rate of cell division. If the same holds true of higher organisms like man, which is not certain, we have a medical problem to solve before starting long space voyages. A human being has a lifespan so much greater than a bacterium's that the changed rate may not bother him. But we must find out.

Plants, similarly, appeared to have grown about half again as fast as they would have done on Earth. That is good news; as we shall see, interplanetary craft may need their own gardens. But the roots of these young plants became a disorderly tangle and the leaves did not reach out in normal directions. Maybe we shall have to breed new kinds that can flourish in orbit.

The fertilized frog eggs seemed to have developed in an ordinary fashion. The insects looked quite healthy, and this in spite of having been given high doses of radiation. Insects always resist it better than men. But we are glad to think that the resistance of any animal is not lowered by weightlessness.

These results are all tentative. Some may prove to be erroneous. A lengthy series of tests lies ahead before we can speak with assurance about living in space. But we have made a good beginning.

In fact, the prospects are so encouraging that the United

States is going ahead with its Manned Orbiting Laboratory. Although this will be constructed and operated by the Department of Defense rather than NASA, it should be even more valuable to civilians than to the military.

An artist's conception of a manned orbiting laboratory. Men will be able to live and work in an earthlike atmosphere aboard such an orbiting workshop for up to a month.

Part of the MOL will be the modified Gemini capsule in which the astronauts ride out and home again. But while aloft, that vehicle will be coupled to a permanently orbiting cylinder, 41 feet long and 10 feet across. Within this volume, a pair of men should be able to live in "shirtsleeves" for periods up to 30 days. They will carry out assignments that only men, not instruments or robots, can do. The initial flights are scheduled for 1968.

Thus, the MOL will be an embryo space station. Perhaps it will not be the first. There is reason to think that the Soviets plan to establish one or more of their own.

The uses of an orbital station, where men can settle for a good while and work with elbow room and adequate tools, are many. Military surveillance and scientific research come to mind at once. But the far future may remember the stations as the first stepping stones to the outer universe.

Of course, before we get too ambitious, we must build far more than an MOL. We shall want a very large satellite, possibly miles across, holding workshops and space docks as well as laboratories. It must house scores or even hundreds of people, and give them sufficient comfort and privacy that they won't mind spending months at a time there.

This is not as fantastic as it sounds. The station can be built gradually. The parts that are first completed can be in use before the rest of the structure has been finished, like a house in which people live while new rooms are being added. The station can have a comparatively low mass. After all, most of its volume will be hollow. Where there is no weight, it can be made of extremely light, though tough, materials. Much if not all of its power can be taken directly from the sun with the help of large mirrors and solar cells. It should be possible for the station to produce its own air and water and some of its own food. Therefore, once constructed, it should not be expensive to maintain.

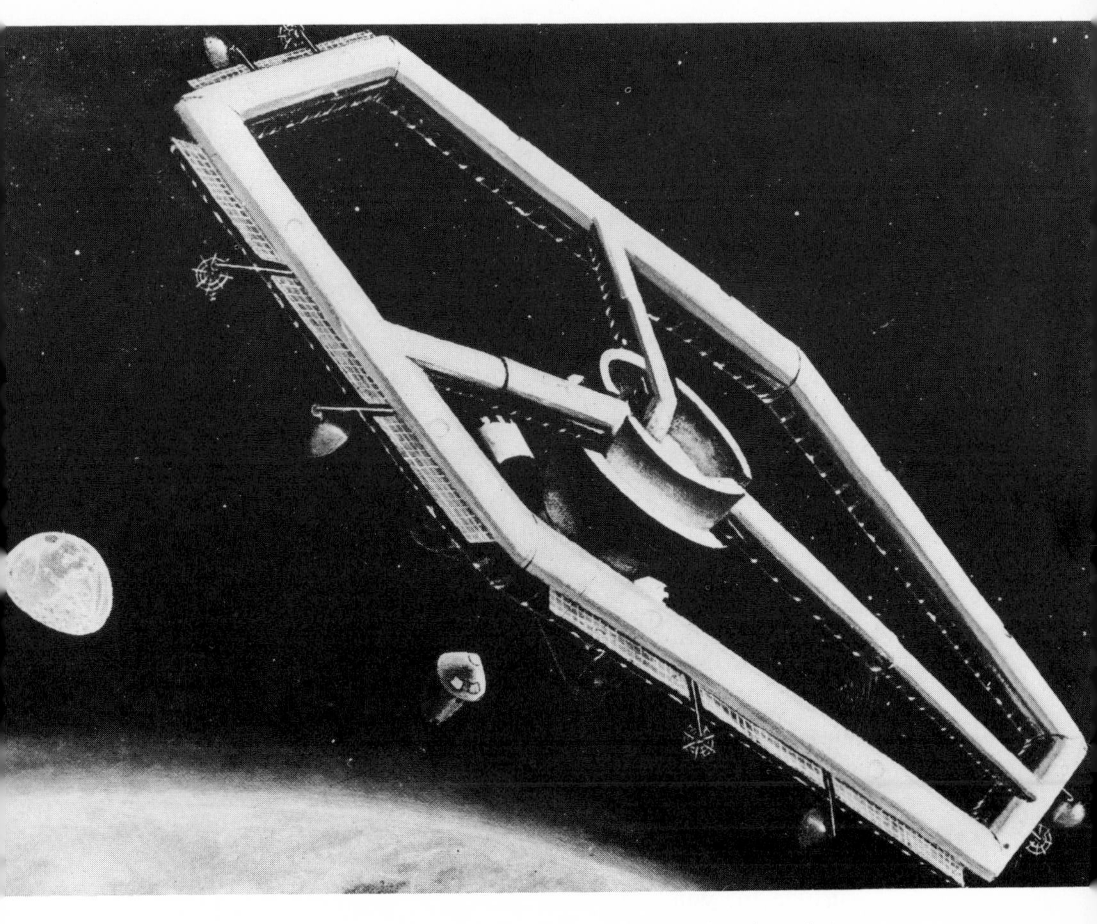

Future orbiting space stations may look like this design based on studies by NASA and North American Aviation. Such stations may be the first stepping stones to the universe.

If radiation and zero gravity turn out to be dangerous, a space station can offer protection. Small thick-walled shelters can be included. There, people can ride out a solar storm, cramped but safe. As for weight, a spaceship might provide that for its crew by substituting centrifugal force for gravitational pull. In a large, probably wheel-shaped station, it should be easier yet to supply weight by spinning the whole structure.

Besides its value as a research center, the station has the tremendous advantage of being in orbit. If fairly close to Earth, it is moving at five miles per second. A ship leaving it need therefore gain only two miles a second to escape from our planet completely. Thus, in the earlier stages of exploring the Solar System, the station can be an indispensable refueling base for vessels that have boosted from the ground. Later on, with more experience and better spacecraft, the larger ones will simply dock there and never touch the planetary surface. Small ferries will bring their crews up from Earth and down again at far less cost.

When atomic-powered ships are on hand, they will doubtless continue to use the orbital berths. For one thing, their blasts might contaminate Earth with radioactivity. Even if this does not prove to be true, the captains and owners will be reluctant to spend fuel on an unnecessary landing. And, finally, the deep-spacecraft of the farther future may never be able to land. They may be too big.

These giant vessels are thought of as being made of light materials like the stations, thin-ribbed and thin-skinned. Although sturdy enough, a ship of this kind would have an enormous surface for wind to strike, especially in proportion to its mass. Entering an atmosphere could be too risky for it. Or, in spite of its construction, it might be so big that the total weight would be too great for liftoff.

None of these problems exist if the ships are built in orbit in the first place. But this requires a station nearby, where tools and supplies are kept, parts fabricated, workmen housed.

It is thrilling to imagine the project. Earth glows immense among the constellations. Space-suited humans flit about the frame of a titan that may be intended to reach one of those stars. Torches flare, hammers strike without sound in airlessness, the rockets of a backpack snort white vapor as one man hauls a weightless ton of girder into place, the radio waves crackle with voices. And in the background, domed, turreted, masted, its light-warm windows streaming as the huge wheel shape gently rotates—there is the station that made it all possible, man's new city in the heavens.

CHAPTER 6

Lunar Frontier

Necessary though spatial outposts will be to our exploration of the universe, they are not the complete solution. Limitations of size and resources will always put bounds on their usefulness. After we have enough of them, or even earlier, we must begin to settle other worlds. The nearest is the moon. Project Apollo should not mark the only time that men set foot there, but the first. In due course, we ought to establish at least one permanent colony.

Many people will ask, "Why?" or "How?" or both. At first glance, the moon seems to offer no attractions and infinite obstacles. Indeed, it looks like a death trap.

With about one-fourth the diameter of Earth, and lower density, it has about one-eightieth the mass. Hence, its gravity at the surface is a mere one-sixth of what we are used to. The escape velocity, as we remarked earlier, is 1.5 miles per second, compared to Earth's 7. Accordingly, it has no atmosphere. If ever it did in the beginning, this was lost to space. Without air pressure upon them, any lakes and seas that there were boiled, became vapor, and were likewise lost. What gas remains must be the faintest trace, too little to detect with Earthbound instruments. To all intents and purposes, the moon is wrapped in utter vacuum.

The effects go beyond simply forcing astronauts to wear spacesuits outside their LEM. Air and water moderate temperature. During a two-week day, the moonlands scorch at more than 200° F. Then night falls almost instantly, since there is nothing to scatter sunlight to make a long dusk. The temperature of those naked rocks plummets close to absolute zero, the deepest possible cold, —460° F. (If it is actually a few tens of degrees higher, that makes no practical difference.) Protection against such extremes is harder to devise than it is in orbit. On the ground, heat is transferred by conduction, a flow of energy through matter, as well as by radiation, a flow of energy through space.

Another type of radiation, the charged particles and X-rays that can be so deadly, presents another menace. No miles of air will shield us as at home. Nor will an extensive magnetic field deflect many particles before they come within hundreds of miles. Probes and robots, such as the Russian Lunik and the American Surveyor, confirmed that the moon has little or no magnetism.

Earth's kindly sky also guards us from meteoroids, pieces of cosmic rock and metal that strike at the rate of thousands per day and miles per second. None but the very largest reach the surface before friction has reduced them to gas, and even these have lost size and energy. Every single one that collides with the moon does so with its full original momentum. While the vast majority are exceedingly small, and the likelihood of any hitting a man is less than astronomers once believed, nevertheless here is another hazard.

Without air to transmit sound, the moon is silent. Radio is under a severe handicap. For lack of a reflecting upper atmosphere, its waves will not normally go past the lunar horizon.

Instead, they will continue straight on into space. And on that small world, the horizon is near, only about a mile and a half for someone standing on a flat plain.

A man cannot travel far unless he is to lose touch with his companions. And this he will scarcely dare do. In a wild, little-known, trickily lit environment, trouble strikes fast and hard. A leak in a spacesuit or vehicle, letting air escape, means doom unless it is quickly repaired. If his electric car breaks down, the astronaut might not be able to return on foot. Heat, cold, radiation, cliffs, and crevasses may forbid this. Or the distance may be so great that he will use up all the oxygen he can carry on his back before he is through. Hence, the earlier lunar expeditions, at least, must operate on a short tether.

These are some of the reasons for asking, "How?" Is exploration possible, except for a trip as brief as Apollo's? We must next ask, "Why?" What lies among those barren lava deserts, stark mountains, monstrous craters to draw us?

Treasure? No. Even if the surface were covered with gold and diamonds, the cost of mining would be far above their value —if that were our sole motive for going there. Besides, Surveyor probes, partially analyzing the rock where they landed, report nothing but common basalt and the like.

Military bases? No. Quite apart from the treaty forbidding them, they would have no usefulness that was not grotesquely outweighed by the expense and trouble.

Scientific research? Can we not carry this out more cheaply, easily, and safely by sending improved unmanned vehicles, robots programmed to find answers to our questions?

No. We cannot. A machine does only what it is supposed to do—at best. It stands helpless before the unforeseen. We know so little about the moon that no one can guess everything we might want to learn there. What are a few of the riddles that require humans to answer them?

The first several deal with the moon itself. What is that alien sphere really like, especially below the surface? What structures have the rocks, and how many kinds? What goes on in the interior? Whence came the thousands of craters that pock the face? Are they all from meteorites, or did volcanoes play a role? Is there still an occasional volcanic outburst? Are certain areas covered with dust? Does some water remain, as in the form of underground ice? What produced the maria, the dark level areas, and why do they seem to be concentrated on the Earthward side? The mysteries are endless. In solving them, we will learn not about the moon alone, but about the cosmos as a whole.

In fact, we will indirectly be studying Earth, notably Earth's distant past. Was the moon once pulled out of the body of our planet, or was it a captured stray, or did the two form together? Whatever has happened, how did it happen? Without weather to erode rocks, the moon surely preserves more clues to the origin and the early days of the Solar System than Earth does.

Among them may be clues to the origin of life. Germs, carried by winds into the upper atmosphere, could well be driven by the pressure of sunlight—small but real—into space. A few would land on the moon. Radiation would disintegrate them, unless they fell into a crack, mingled with a dust layer, or otherwise got protection. But quite likely some would. They would amount, perhaps, to no more than several hundred per year. However, in a billion years or more, these dead germs would add up to many, preserved in a condition that would enable scientists to examine them. So it seems plausible that the moon is rich in remnants that will help us understand how life began.

Perhaps these traces, if we find them, will turn out to be largely from the moon itself. It may have kept some air and liquid water long enough for primitive organisms to get started. A third possibility is a cosmic source. Life certainly did not originate in the vast dust cloud that we believe condensed to make the Solar System. But various complex materials that go into living things may have been generated there.

Two views of the moon, showing the Tycho crater. The top photograph was taken from Earth, the bottom from Lunar Orbiter V.

Wherever the organic stuff came from, if it does exist, the moon has vacuum-preserved it for us to study.

Conceivably, we may find more than microscopic smears, smudges, and fossils. Could there be life on the moon today? Most scientists believe not. Yet some microbes, whether lunar natives or earthly immigrants, may have adapted sufficiently fast to those harsh conditions that they survived. Evolution may then have gone on to produce new varieties. No one expects anything large-sized. But however small and simple, life on the moon or inside it would open whole new universes to science.

On the practical side, again, we should observe that a deeper understanding of life in general will help us make further progress in medicine. True, we may discover that the moon holds nothing biological, not even traces. But that fact would itself point toward a greater truth. And in any event, we won't know until we have tried!

This is why the vehicles that have landed there were carefully sterilized before they left. We do not want confusing contamination of the lunar environment by modern Earth bacteria, before we have had a chance to investigate its natural condition.

Besides being fascinating and important in its own right, the moon is a place to do things that are difficult or impossible elsewhere. Giant telescopes, unhampered by air, can probe the deeper secrets of the galaxies. To be sure, such instruments can simply be put in orbit, and doubtless will be. However, the moon is so stable and slow-moving a platform as to offer numerous special advantages. It will be priceless to radio astronomers. Tuning in the "broadcasts" of the stars, they have already learned an enormous amount. Nevertheless, interference hampers them. They could get away from atmospheric static in orbit, but not from radio, television, radar, and other man-made noise. On the side of the moon that is perpetually turned away, they will have its whole bulk for a shield.

Electronics engineers will be delighted with all that vacuum, plus solid ground underfoot. They will carry out tests and research far more rapidly and easily, on a far larger scale, than on a planet where they are limited to pumped-out chambers. The same applies to nuclear physicists, chemists, metallurgists, and every other kind of scientist. As for the biologists, though free fall will let them discover the effects of weightlessness, what about prolonged *low* weight?

With a little imagination, anyone can think of endless other exciting fields of discovery. The knowledge gained, and the everyday benefits flowing from the use of that knowledge, will sooner or later richly repay the investment, and probably sooner rather than later. But plain to see, programs as ambitious as these cannot be carried out by sending a few men for a few hours at a time, years apart. Instead, people must settle down to spend months, years, maybe whole lifetimes on the moon. And they must have ample supplies and equipment.

Can this be done, though? Considering how long and expensive our three-part lunar landing project is, are we not daydreaming when we imagine hundreds of expeditions bringing many tons of cargo each?

Well, ours is a pioneering effort, and such are always more difficult than the follow-up. Later trips will be so much easier by comparison that we would be foolish not to take advantage of the opportunity. Along the way, we will gain techniques for carrying bigger payloads more cheaply and safely than now. For instance, instead of throwing away the booster at each launching, we will learn how to recover and reuse this expensive machine. The rocket motors themselves will be greatly improved. Orbital refueling is another possibility.

Furthermore, the need for making shipments to the moon will diminish after a while. Once a colony is well-established, it can and should begin to furnish more and more of its own needs. In time, it should become self-supporting, and finally, a net producer of wealth for mankind.

After all, every element that exists on Earth must be present on the moon. The proportions of the elements to each other, the ores in which they occur, perhaps differ from world to world. But while Earth may once have been richer in some of them, we have gutted our best lodes. Untouched, the moon almost certainly holds Golcondas and Mesabis of metals. The chances are that, in airlessness, they are less thoroughly combined with other elements than they are here. So they ought to need less refining.

It is also possible to obtain important chemicals, like sulfuric acid, from lunar materials. This includes water. As we have seen, caverns and rock layers may hold ice deposits. Sealed away from vacuum, insulated from heat, they could be extensive. But if we find none, we can extract water from rocks in which it is crystallized. The Surveyor data give us good reason to expect that such rocks are lunar as well as earthly. Besides being a necessity of life, water breaks down under an electric current to hydrogen and oxygen. The second of these gases we breathe. The two together can recombine in a fuel cell or a motor to furnish power.

There might even be oil in the moon. Some astronomers theorize that most of the organic substances in petroleum originated in the ancient dust cloud. If so, lunar wells are a valuable future resource. Men will scarcely ship that oil back to Earth. Instead, they will use it not only for fuel, but as a starting point for synthesizing other materials, plastics, medicines, fertilizers, foods.

Again, we are not dependent on such a lucky break. The colony can get along with raw minerals. From their atoms, its advanced chemical engineering can produce whatever is needed.

No doubt the colonists will soon turn from imported rations and local imitations to the best food producers of all, namely, plants and animals. Besides furnishing natural products for the table, plants keep the air in balance. Taking in the carbon dioxide and water vapor that we exhale, they release the oxygen that we must inhale. In fact, this process of photosynthesis will help in many ways, some of them quite subtle, to make the environment livable.

Let us, then, visit Luna City in our minds, fifty or a hundred years from now when it is thriving.

Its superstructure covers the floor of a crater. That is not one of the giants like Copernicus, whose ringwall is under the horizon when you stand at the center. Smaller, but tall and rugged enough, this circular cliff surrounds the flat bottom like the fortifications of a medieval castle. Indeed, it does afford protection against the unlikely event of a glancing meteoroid strike or an accident in the spaceport outside. But principally it gives a wider range to the radio and radar masts built on its heights. Operating with several synchronous relay satellites, these provide communications over the whole moon, and with the Earth that hangs gigantic above.

Descending, we see a network of roads radiating from the crater. They are rather sketchily made; nothing better is required in low gravity and the absence of weathering. Along them moves heavy traffic. Except for some purely automatic ones, the vehicles are driven by men in sealed cabins. They vary widely. Among them we notice a tractor hauling a train of ore wagons from the rich iron mines; a prospector's car, with balloon tires and auxiliary legs for rough country; and the regular bus from Farside Station, where the radio observatory is.

The most impressive sight outside the crater is a launching rack. Miles long, its gleaming rails use electric power to accelerate spaceships past the moon's low escape velocity. The saving in fuel helps make travel inexpensive. (It also reduces the contamination of the local vacuum by exhaust gases. Even so, several research labs have moved hundreds of miles away, with much grumbling.) A vessel bound for Earth spends little fuel, because the atmosphere brakes it at the other end of the trip in a series of gentle spirals.

Moon colonies, forty years from now, may look like the one in this drawing. A plastic dome will protect gardens for growing plants that will stabilize an earthlike atmosphere.

What does the moon export to Earth? Returning scientists, engineers, and tourists, for one! Then there are certain types of electronic gear that can only be made with the necessary precision in this large-scale emptiness. The same holds true of extracts from specially bred life forms, and supergiant molecules compounded in chemical vats. Both must have low gravity to develop. These products are wanted chiefly in medicine, though computermen are getting interested in them, too, as data storage units. We hear talk that the bustling, booming lunar industries will soon find it profitable to ship larger items, such as molecular-bonded honeycomb modules assembled in vacuum for structural uses.

Despite all that activity, energy remains cheap here. Besides atomic power, chemical fuels, and the rest, we have the sun. For half a month at a time, it shines undimmed and uninterrupted, pouring better than a horsepower per square yard into efficient solar cells. These convert the energy into storable forms. Some holds off the cold of night. But surprisingly little goes for that, Luna City being well insulated. And so most is available for other purposes.

The insulation of the colony is largely due to its underground location. The crater floor is covered with man-made facilities. And, given reliable modern equipment, men travel quite freely on the surface. But most of Luna City stays nestled beneath yards of rock, safe from heat, cold, radiation, and meteoroids. It expands by digging tunnels and artificial caves.

It is anything but gloomy, though. Fluorescent panels flood it with light. The colors are cheerful, the furnishing comfortable. The air smells sweet from the many plants that seem to grow wherever we look. To tell the truth, the main work of photosynthesis is done by homely little algae in tanks. But the Lunarians appreciate flowers more than Earthlings do.

Besides their occupations, the people keep busy with imaginative forms of recreation. Remember, they were selected to come here because they are unusually able and intelligent. They enjoy direct beamcasts from Earth of everything interesting; they also have their own tapes, libraries, art galleries, symphony orchestra, theater, museums, handicrafts, and sports. More children are born every year, which means they need schools. The social atmosphere is a curious blend of scholarship, enthusiasm, small-town intimacy, and civic pride.

As in science and industry, so in athletics are things done that could never be done on Earth. You weigh only one-sixth as much here. It is not an entirely unmixed blessing. Your mass has not changed. So the balance between your downward-pressing weight and your first-law tendency to keep moving in a straight line is altered. Newcomers often have trouble before they get the knack of walking and running. Once they do, they feel a marvelous, bounding, high-soaring lightness. A ball, thrown or batted horizontally, travels far. Anything cast upward rises high and comes down slowly. This has forced changes in the rules of games like soccer and basketball.

The most spectacular lunar sport was foreseen back in the twentieth century by Robert Heinlein. Under weak gravity but normal air pressure, human muscles have the strength for flight. With pedals driving a propeller, or wings strapped to your arms, you soar about in high-ceilinged parks. Real birds, that nest in the trees below, move like little rockets.

Excursions aboveground are the favorite pastime. Many a young person goes topside simply to look at the night stars and dream. For Luna City's whole existence is aimed heavenward.

Now that the colony is self-sufficient, it imports little from Earth. Its exports to the mother world are not critically important either. What the moon has become is the principal supplier to the space stations. A load of metals, chemicals, food, anything, can go from a launch rack here to an orbiting settlement at almost no cost in fuel. This applies to rocket fuel itself, now manufactured exclusively on the moon out of local substances.

Therefore it is the lunar colony which, in the long run, makes those flying cities possible, and makes frequent deep-space trips practical. The people on the moon know with joy that their resources and skills are indispensable. When man stands firmly on Earth's companion, he can reach out as often as he likes to Mars, Venus, Pluto, even, it may be, to other stars.

CHAPTER

7

From Argo to Starship

More than three thousand years ago, says the legend, the hero Jason sailed his ship *Argo* from Greece to Colchis in search of the Golden Fleece. That was a voyage almost to the ends of the known universe, and he and his crew had many a hairbreadth adventure with strange peoples and nonhuman beings. To this day, their journey symbolizes all long quests into foreign realms. The name bestowed upon them, Argonauts, inspired our words astronaut and cosmonaut.

It may seem a far cry from a little galley bobbing on Mediterranean waves to a huge, sleek, galaxy-spanning spaceship like those about which so many science fiction stories have been written. But in reality the comparison is close. Argonaut and astronaut alike venture forth where nothing is foreknown, where distances engulf them and their craft, where immense blind forces may destroy them, where danger and terror may lurk—but where surely the joy of discovery and service awaits.

We had better admit too that both these ships are mythical. No one knows if there was a historical Jason. Nor does anyone know if there will ever be anything like a star ship. In either case, the most we can do is assemble the facts and make some intelligent guesses on that basis.

When we look beyond the moon, we see the abysses really opening up. The nearest planet, Venus, never comes closer to Earth than about 26 million miles. That is more than 100 times the distance to the moon. Suppose we departed with a velocity of 1 mile per second, this being what was left after we had lost 7 miles per second in rising directly from Earth or 2 in breaking free of orbit. We would spend some 10 months on the crossing.

Matters are not that simple. The separation of planets is continuously changing as they move around the sun at their different rates. A spaceship cannot travel in a straight line at constant speed. Its path is influenced by too many factors. These include its velocity and position when it started out, the extent to which it uses rocket power, and the gravitational attractions of the sun and any nearby celestial bodies. But our example gives a rough idea of the time involved in interplanetary expeditions of the near future.

The vessels will accelerate as much as fuel supplies allow. Once in the correct trajectory, they must fall free until they near the goal. At that point, they will maneuver themselves into orbit around the target planet. Rather than landing massive ships, the crews will almost certainly send down small vehicles carrying one or a few men each, intended to return and dock somewhat like the LEM.

The explorers will not be able to start back whenever they wish. That would usually take too long, or they would run out of fuel, or both. Instead, they will wait until Earth is in a favorable position with respect to the world where they are. The homeward passage will last approximately, though not exactly, as long as the outward one, and will likewise be made mostly in free fall. Altogether, months or years will go by between the moment the astronauts depart Earth and the moment of their homecoming.

The time of transit can be shortened, perhaps eventually to a few days. But expeditions will still need a schedule that lets them get some real work done.

So, no matter how powerful a motor we build, the mastery of space demands that our pioneers spend extended periods aboard spacecraft. Can they?

Plain to see, the ship has to be larger than the Apollo command module. Not only must it carry tons of equipment and supplies, it must provide some elbow room, some chance for recreation and relaxation. Otherwise, the crew could not endure their surroundings. If they did not die or go insane, they would at least be in no fit condition for anything before long. Hence, the first requirement is an engine capable of moving that great a mass around the Solar System.

We have already seen that interplanetary missions will probably start from Earth orbit, where they need only about 2 miles per second to escape. Given this head start, Saturn 5 could send a considerable payload to another world. Engineers have done some design work on yet more awesome boosters, like the projected Nova. This 300-foot, 4 million-pound multistager, whose first stage will exert 12 million pounds of thrust, should be able to put 90,000 pounds into Mars orbit.

It may never be built, though. Everyone agrees that the best solution lies not in chemical fuels but in atomic energy. The latter has fantastically greater power. For instance, when one atom of uranium-235 fissions, it releases better than 20 million times the energy of a burnt molecule of gasoline. A well-designed atomic rocket will not use anything like the amount of fuel that a Saturn does. Nevertheless, it will accelerate to far greater velocities. It will not carry liquid-gas tanks, or a lot of other cumbersome apparatus. The mass saved can go into payload.

In short, nothing but atomic power can make interplanetary

voyages quick and easy. The very first, crude atomic ships ought to be superior to any of their chemical forerunners. Maybe they will be available before we get around to constructing monsters like Nova.

Scientists think seriously about two distinct ways of applying atomic energy to rockets. One method would use a nuclear reactor to heat up a suitable material, which might be a metal, or a room-temperature liquid, conceivably ordinary water. (This reaction mass, as it is called to distinguish it from energy-supplying fuel, could best be obtained from the moon.) Turned to vapor by the enormous temperature, the material would rush out of the nozzles with correspondingly enormous speed. Not much would be needed for a spaceship to reach high velocities. This system is now under development, and looks hopeful.

More difficult to make, but more promising in the long run, is the ion drive. An engine of this sort would also vaporize the reaction mass. But the temperature would be no greater than necessary to do that, because the energy of the reaction mass would be supplied otherwise than by heat. The gas would pass through a powerful electric arc that would turn its atoms into ions. An ion is an atom or group of combined atoms that carries an electric charge. Cosmic radiation, such as the sun emits during a storm, consists mainly of positive ions and free electrons.

The ions of reaction mass would then pass down a series of rings, probably outside the hull. Electric and magnetic fields in these rings would accelerate the ions just as happens in one of the machines with which physicists bombard atoms. The stream would be traveling extremely fast when finally released, much faster than the first kind of motor can manage. This system also ought to be more flexible and readily controllable than the first one.

Advanced spaceships of the farther future might well eject matter at almost the speed of light. That would enable them to attain huge velocities at small cost. For instance, given an ion blast this rapid, we would exhaust little more than 100 pounds in accelerating a ton to 10,000 miles per second.

The ultimate ejection speed would be that of light itself, a beam of pure energy rather than matter. But at present, we know of no way to make this, not even in theory.

Atomic power does have certain drawbacks. The main one is the deadly radiation that comes off as a byproduct. A reactor must be heavily shielded if life is to go on anywhere near it. A superenergetic system like one of those we have described will mean carrying a lot of dead weight along for protection.

We can reduce that mass by building the ship to keep men and motor a goodly distance apart. Arthur C. Clarke, the well-known science writer, has proposed a dumbbell-shaped vessel. The forward sphere holds living and working quarters, the after one holds powerplant and reaction mass, probably with a derrick-like ion accelerator jutting from the stern. The "bar" between the globes is really a hollow cylinder. It contains an adequate lead barricade. Forward of this, we stow in the cylinder such gear as will not be damaged by radiation; this acts as extra shielding.

Ungraceful though it appears, the craft could get about quite handily. And so could a number of other forms, round, egg-shaped, pencil-shaped, indeed almost anything. Space offers no air resistance, and the larger ships will never land. We can therefore design them with other features in mind than streamlining.

The design must also embody safeguards against cosmic radiation when that gets too intense. No doubt the hull structure will include a certain amount of shielding. The ship might carry a small thick-walled shelter for emergencies, as we have suggested the space station will. Someday, scientists hope, no armor will be needed except a thin plating to stop X-rays. Instead, spacecraft will carry generators that enclose them in magnetic fields so strong that no charged particle can penetrate. But to date, we cannot build that effective an electromagnet.

The ship must provide against meteoroids, too. While most of these rocks are harmless because of being very small, all travel at miles per second. If a large one hit, say with a mass of several pounds, it would go straight through the hull. That need not be fatal. Air would not escape instantaneously. A crewman could slap a patch over each hole. The air's own pressure would keep the patches in place until the men made a real repair. As for minute punctures, less easy to find, we can build the hull like a self-sealing gasoline tank. Gluey material, compressed between two layers of metal, hardens when exposed and stops the leak.

Temperature control has nothing to do with the "terrible cold of space" that people formerly dreaded. Space is neither hot nor cold. Temperature is a property of matter, not of vacuum. Experience shows that it is not too difficult to keep a ship's cabin comfortable in the neighborhood of Earth, Mars, and Venus.

Farther from the sun, the powerplant must furnish some extra heat to make up for what the vessel radiates away. Closer, we face the opposite and worse problem. How do we get rid of the energy that the nearby sun is pouring on us? We can obtain some relief from a shiny outside paint that reflects back most of what falls on it. It we go as far inward as the orbit of Mercury, this may not suffice. We may have to develop something else, like a sophisticated thermistor system, or carry a lot of refrigerant that cools the living quarters as it boils away into space.

A ship alone will not keep our astronauts alive. What supplies should they bring?

A man doing light work, and not overeating, consumes a little over one pound of food daily, five pounds of water, and two pounds of oxygen. (We are supposing the food is freeze-dried, so that much of the water goes into preparing it.) On short expeditions like Apollo, it is most efficient simply to take along this eight or nine pounds per man per day and throw the waste products into space. But on months-long missions, with tens or scores of crewpeople, that makes a prohibitive tonnage. We shall have to reuse our materials.

This we can do, in the same way as the orbital stations and the lunar colony. Plants take in the carbon dioxide and water vapor that animals like man give off. With the help of a few chemicals, and of light, they rebuild these substances into the molecules of their own tissues. They don't need all the oxygen that was combined originally, so they release this element, renewing the air for the animals. It seems to take about eleven square feet of green leaf to keep a man at rest in oxygen, somewhat more if he is working.

To take advantage of this, we must first learn how to grow plants in space. The Biosatellite project is a bare beginning. We do not know either, today, what kinds of plants are best. As our imaginary picture of Luna City hinted, algae may be preferable to pumpkins or berry bushes. The algae are a large and hardy class, including most sea weeds, plus smaller forms that make the scum on stagnant ponds or give brilliant colors to the hot springs of Yellowstone.

The plants can dispose of human waste, using it for fertilizer. The humans, in turn, can eat some of the plants. Although the thought may shock Americans a little at first, it is a perfectly clean and natural process. In fact, it is the basic cycle of life on Earth.

Besides, the system will have to be far more complex and indirect than we might think. A spaceman cannot scoop a handful of slimy brown algae out of a tank for his lunch. It would not provide him with everything his body needs, including tastiness. No doubt numerous sorts of vegetables will be included as well as animals. The animals might be fish, shrimp, and similar things. The food will be prepared in various ways. Probably certain vitamins and minerals must be carried along. But their mass is not great, even for a trip of several years. The same is true of the herbs and spices that make an otherwise plain meal appetizing.

In the farther future, space-borne "farms" will become obsolete. A computer-guided chemical machine will see to everything. We may even have such machines before we are ready to embark on our first interplanetary expeditions. Biochemistry is progressing fast nowadays. In any event, whatever the exact method, we know that it is possible to keep a spaceship livable indefinitely.

But what about weightlessness? Can exercise alone keep off its harmful effects? Might not months of free fall cripple or kill the astronauts?

We have no final answer at present. Maybe weightlessness is not injurious. Maybe it is. It definitely creates a lot of nuisances. We would like to furnish our crew with an "up" and "down."

Science knows two ways by which this might be done. The first is spinning the ship.

In the illustration of a ball whirled at the end of a string around a boy's head, centrifugal force tugs the ball outward. The same force pushes us toward the side of a car when it takes a curve. Stunt motorcyclists rely on it when, through sheer speed, they ride around and around on a steeply banked wall. Giant centrifuges test human volunteers by spinning them to learn how much weight a man can endure.

Centrifugal force acts quite similarly to gravity. It is proportional to the radius of spin and the number of turns in a given time. For example, if two identical balls whirl around at the same rate, but one is on a string twice as long as the other, then it, the first one, has twice the centrifugal force on it that the second one does. Likewise, if the strings are of equal length, but one ball goes around twice as many times in a second as the other, again the first one experiences twice the force.

Suppose our spaceship is a hollow cylinder, that being the easiest shape to visualize. And suppose it rotates on its stem-to-stern axis. If it has a radius of ten feet, and turns once in about

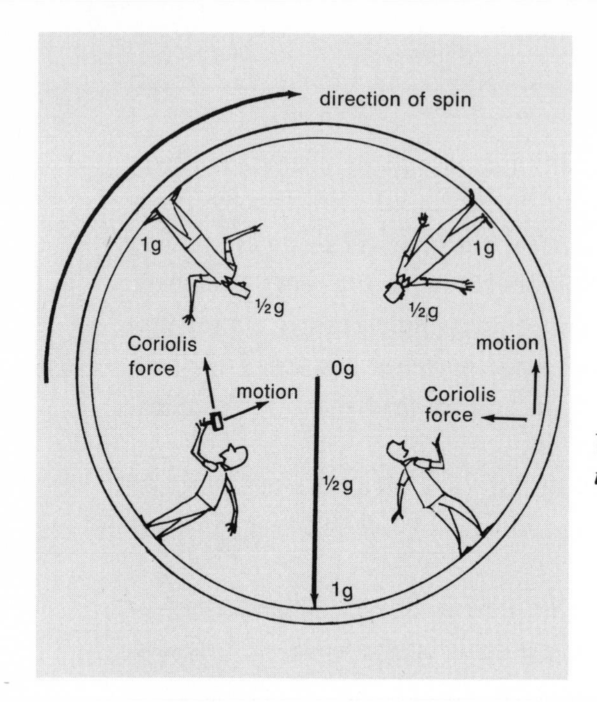

Weight and Coriolis force in a rotating spaceship.

three seconds, centrifugal force at the wall is equal to Earth sea-level gravity. Now the axis of the cylinder does not rotate; and halfway between it and the wall—five feet from either—the spin radius is halved. Therefore the force is also halved. A spaceman standing inside this ship would have his feet at normal weight but his head at only half this. Every movement up or down would take him through a series of changes that might make him feel sick.

In addition, Coriolis force would plague him. This is a force generated by motion inside a turning system. It works at right angles to that motion. If our astronaut picked a tool straight up from a table, Coriolis force would give that tool a forward tug. Although not too powerful to overcome, it would add another annoyance.

The greater the radius, the slower our cylinder need rotate to produce one gravity at the wall. That reduces Coriolis force, which depends on the rate of spin, not on the radius. It also reduces weight change with height. Suppose the cylinder, instead of being a mere 10 feet across, were 100 feet across: that is,

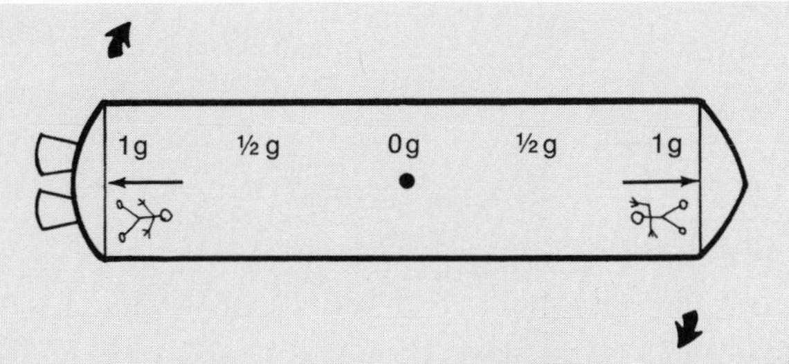

The distribution of weight when a spaceship rotates end over end.

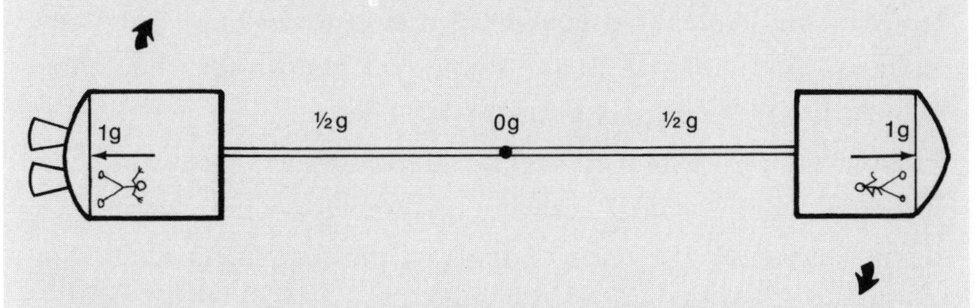

The weight when a divided spaceship rotates around a cable.

that there were 50 feet from wall to center. Then our astronaut would experience only a 10 percent difference in the weight factor between feet and head. This would probably not bother him. Given, say, a 1,000-foot spin radius, he might scarcely notice the slight variations or the weak Coriolis forces.

Orbital stations may well grow to diameters of several miles. We aren't likely to build spaceships that big for a few hundred years, if ever. But we can find other ways to give them a large spin radius. One method is to rotate them, not around a stem-to-stern axis, but from end to end around the middle. A ship that is not thick could still be quite long. Men in the forward end would then feel "down" as being toward the nose of the ship. Aft of the center, "down" would be in the opposite direction.

Another way of increasing the spin radius is to separate the ship while it is free falling between planets into two halves joined by a cable that could be a mile or more in length. This system then whirls around the midpoint of the cable. For a one-mile separation, one turn in 24 minutes provides Earthlike weight at the two ends. At present, the mass of a cable like this is too great to be practical. But lighter and stronger wire should be available in the future.

Spin is not the only method of providing weight. Linear acceleration does it too, and better.

By linear acceleration we mean an increase of velocity in a straight line. A car that goes from a stop to 10 miles per hour in one second, or from 20 to 30 miles per hour in the same time, is linearly accelerating at a rate of 10 miles per hour per second. Meanwhile, the passengers feel themselves drawn backward. The force on them is called acceleration pressure. Their bodies are being pushed by the mass of the car, bringing them up to the same speed that the car is acquiring.

Earth's gravity, near the surface, accelerates everything downward at the rate of 32 feet per second per second. That is, if you fall freely, you travel each second at 32 feet per second faster than before. That may not look like much, but it adds 60 miles per hour in less than three seconds. This rate is known as one "gravity," or one g.

An accelerating vehicle presses on its passengers, and they press back. The force is transmitted to every part of both. And so a spaceship gaining speed at one g would give its passengers the same weight as they have at home. "Down" would always be straight aft, opposite to the direction of movement. There would be no weight variation, Coriolis force, or other troubles caused by spin. Furthermore, constant acceleration would build up such tremendous velocities that interplanetary crossings would be made in days.

Consider our example of a 26 million-mile journey to Venus. This time we shall travel at a steady one g. Although we won't quite go in a straight line, we will more nearly than when we were orbiting to our goal. We cover half the distance, 13 million miles. By that time we are moving at an incredible 400 miles per second. Not wishing to spatter on arrival, we turn off the thrust for a short period and rotate the ship end for end. Now the

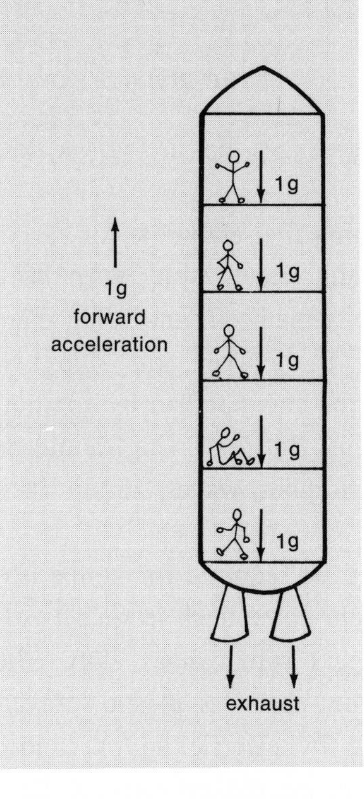

The weight in a spaceship under linear acceleration at the rate of one g would give passengers the same weight they have on Earth.

rockets point toward our objective, and when we fire them they slow us down at the same rate of one g. Weight inside feels no different. We reach Venus with a safe, low speed, 37 hours after we left Earth.

Nothing less than a highly advanced ion-drive vessel can do this. Long before we can build one, we should have atomic-powered ships capable of a constant, though quite small acceleration. Early models are in the designing stage. They will make slower crossings than a one-g racer, and provide correspondingly less weight inboard. But they will enable us to attain the outer planets of the Solar System in a moderate time.

If the sun's family is ever extensively colonized and interplanetary travel becomes commonplace, the entire "space marine" will scarcely tear along at a full gravity. Such ultrapowerful, expensive systems will be for special purposes: patrols, rescue operations, extended scientific missions, and passenger carrying. Today we cannot foretell whether ordinary travelers will ride on the fastest ships. It depends on cost. Perhaps the luxury liners will go at one g, while others offer passages that are slower, less costly, and often more fun.

There is no reason to use something that elaborate for cargo. The chances are that most merchant vessels won't even have crews. Human control gangs will start them off, and bring them in to their destinations, by radio. In between, the ship will simply orbit, with minor course corrections handled by computers. That means they will take months. But the saving should be worth it, in life support apparatus, supplies, wages, atomic fuel, and reaction mass.

Maybe no rockets whatsoever will be required for nonperishable consignments. Sailing ships might come back in space! Admittedly, they won't be square-riggers with canvas aloft. The sails will be huge but exceedingly thin sheets of plastic sprayed with metal. They will be trimmed by electric motors under computer guidance. The "wind" will be the pressure of light from the sun, tiny, but multiplied by square miles of area. By combining its force with the inward "tide" of solar and planetary gravity, a spaceship can tack from place to place. Again, it will spend months in transit. But a large fleet of these comparatively cheap vessels would bring in a steady flow of goods. Farfetched though they sound, they are a definite physical possibility. Engineers have already given them thought.

Let us imagine ourselves on a powered man-carrying spaceship of this future. It is one of the full-gravity craft, because we are bound clear to Saturn. Despite the continuous lightning bolt of energy that drives us, it shows no exhaust flame. The ion jets are too efficient for that. Nor does any sound of power reach us, except as the softest quiver in the air, lost among voices, footfalls, all the bustle of our hurrying little world. We stand at a port—actually, for safety reasons, a television relay—looking at the myriad stars. Among them, Earth still shines brightest, a lovely blue spark with a lesser golden companion. But we see the great planet for which we are headed, too, and turn up the magnification for a look at its rings.

That makes a nearer object visible to us. We crowd around to enjoy the rare glimpse of a sunjammer. Its sail is a shining, spinning disc, kept from buckling by centrifugal force. We cannot make out the hull. That circle dwarfs everything else, though its mass is slight. And it also looks small at its distance, lost amidst the constellations. Yet, it beats bravely up against the sun, an apt symbol of the human race that built it. We feel our loneliness diminish and eagerly look forward to the discoveries we hope to make.

Will any such scene come about in reality? That depends on man. He can do these things, and more, if he really wants to. But will he? Is it going to be worth his while to colonize and traffic among the planets?

CHAPTER

8

The Red World and the White

For the better part of a century, Mars has caused more wonder in the human mind than any other heavenly body. How often have we Earthlings stood on a summer evening to gaze upon its red gleam and feel ourselves in the presence of mystery? For this was the sister globe that might well hold life.

Astronomers created that glamour. They learned Mars was small, 4,200 miles in diameter, its surface gravity 40 percent of Earth's, and was accompanied by two tiny moons. The atmosphere was thin but was definitely there, hazing the view, sometimes raising gigantic dust storms. No lakes or seas were visible, but through telescopes men saw polar caps that grew in summer and shrank in winter. Broad dark markings stood clearly forth upon the reddish-tawny background, defining regions that received exotic names like Syrtis Major, Thaumasia, and Lacus Solis. Their color changes suggested forests and meadows responding to the long seasons.

Although the Martian day is nearly equal to ours, the year is indeed long, 1.88 that of Earth. This is because Mars is the next planet out, revolving at an average distance from the sun of 141 million miles. It must therefore be colder than us at our comfortable 93 million miles. Temperature can be measured through infrared radiation. At noon in the Martian tropics it can go as high as 85° F., as if to make up for plunging below −100° F. at night or clear down to −150° F. at polar midwinter. But this is not too far from Siberian or Antarctic extremes. Surely life could arise, adapt, evolve, and finally become intelligent.

Thousands of stories have been written about Martians. A lot of them remain enjoyable. H. G. Wells visualized the inhabitants as sinister, octopus-like aggressors. The astronomer Percival Lowell believed that the long straight streaks he saw were irrigation canals. This led other writers to depict an ancient society of wise, benign beings, as C. S. Lewis did in *Out of the Silent Planet.* Yet the civilization might have collapsed when conditions grew too severe. The Martians would then, in our era, be barbarians. Edgar Rice Burroughs and Leigh Brackett got many colorful tales out of that idea. More scientifically minded authors did not believe anything human could be native to another planet. The Martians must not only look odd, they could have minds so alien to ours that communication with them was difficult. That inspired Stanley Weinbaum to create Tweel of *A Martian Odyssey*, one of the most convincing and appealing characters in science fiction.

But meanwhile research went on. New knowledge brought discouragement. The Martian "canals" are not lines but disconnected dots. The dark areas are not green but gray. While the polar caps do appear to be frozen water, they are hardly more than hoarfrost. All the water on the Martian surface would not fill the Great Lakes. The atmosphere turns out to be ghostly thin. Its ground-level pressure is estimated at about 8 percent of Earth's. No free oxygen is present. Rather, the air contains an

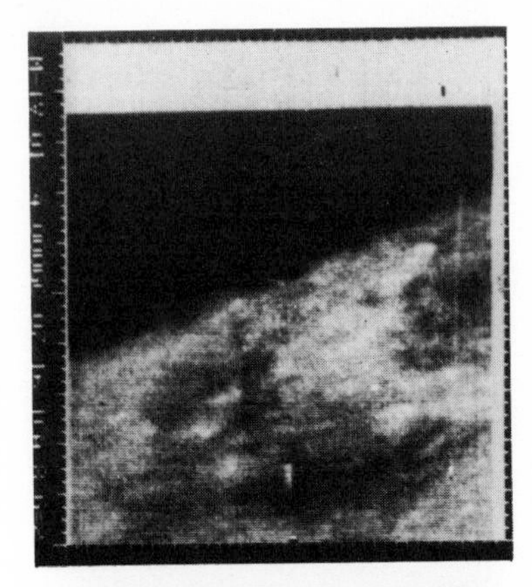

The first Mariner 4 photographs of Mars taken in 1965 in various stages of processing. The photo at left shows maximum detail.

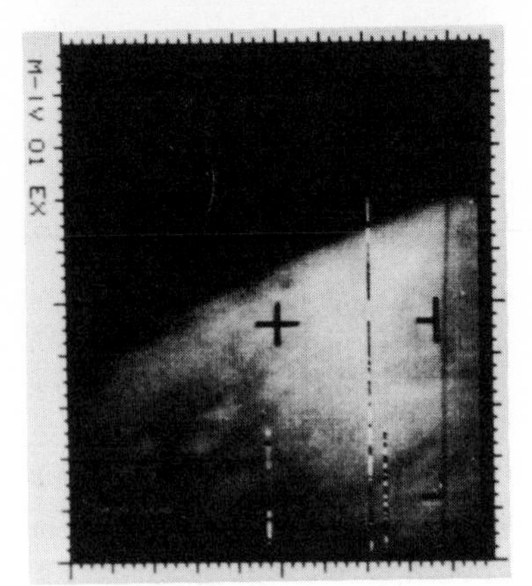

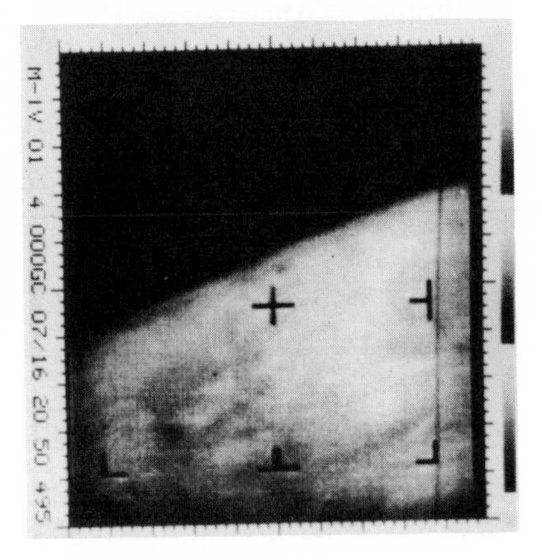

exceedingly high proportion of carbon dioxide. The rest is probably nitrogen and argon. Besides being unbreathable by men, such an atmosphere must pass too much solar ultraviolet light for us.

In 1965, America's Mariner 4 probe sent pictures taken as it flew near Mars. They show a lunar-like landscape of big craters. Nothing in those views hints at anything alive. We have also learned that Mars has a weak magnetic field, if it has any at all. Although solar storms cannot scour the ground as fiercely as they do on our moon, they add another peril.

For a while the scientific journals exhibited a positive bandwagon psychology, as person after person wrote in to explain learnedly how the latest information proved beyond doubt that Mars is dead and always has been. But other articles followed, by equally eminent professionals. They pointed out that it wasn't necessarily so, and that we do have reason to think the planet may harbor life.

Certainly it cannot be our sort of life. It does not have to be totally different from us, though. Experiments have been made in which Martian conditions were simulated in the laboratory as well as knowledge permits. They show that a few kinds of terrestrial microbes and plants can survive. Hence, it is at least possible that our neighbor world bears organisms formed out of proteins as we are.

The craters do not prove the atmosphere is so nearly nonexistent that it cannot weather them away in millions of years. They could be younger than that. This is quite plausible when we recollect that Mars orbits next to the asteroid belt, where large meteoroids are common. The planet must get hit by a big one much more often than Earth or Luna. A strike like that every few centuries will readily account for the Mariner pictures. These, by the way, cover a very limited portion of the globe.

While ultraviolet and cosmic radiation on the surface may be too strong for us to survive without shielding, we know no reason why native life could not have developed protection. It might even depend on those rays, as we do on the sunlight that kills many germs. Martian species could adapt to the cold—by burrowing underground after dark, by having natural "antifreeze" in their body fluids, by developing cells to which nightly freezing is normal and necessary, or by other means that we have not imagined. Oxygen is not always essential. Quite a few microbes on Earth get along without it, and indeed it is poisonous to them. In an environment completely without oxygen, could evolution not make them into something large and complex? Similarly, Martian organisms might not use water. Or if they do, they might need far less than species that developed on this wet Earth.

We do have certain data about Mars that one group of scientists interprets as possible signs of life. They include seasonal changes. As the polar cap melts in spring, a wave of darkening moves toward the equator. It could well be that plants, dormant throughout the winter, now seize the small amount of released water vapor and grow again. Likewise, by examining polarized light, astronomers have found that at this time the dark areas become covered with microbe-sized objects. Are these really living cells? Spectroscopes indicate the presence of organic compounds, hydrocarbons, and aldehydes. They are only traces. But they might come from plants or animals.

The astronomer Carl Sagan remarks that if he has any Martian colleagues, and their instruments are as good as ours, they can discover no better clues to life on Earth. It would be hard to do right in our neighborhood. He examined thousands of pictures taken by weather satellites, much nearer than the 6,118 miles of the closest approach of Mariner 4 to Mars. In only two of them did he find any positive evidence for our planet being inhabited. One showed a grid cut by lumbermen across miles of forest, another the shoulders of a broad new highway. Both will be overgrown and gone from sight in a few years.

Furthermore, if our Martian did see those pictures, he would not know what they meant. Presumably tall trees and long multilane roads are unknown to him. As a cautious scientist, he should conclude that these two untypical scenes result from mere freaks of nature.

Suppose Mars is inhabited, even quite densely inhabited. The life might be so strange that we would have trouble identifying it as such on the ground, let alone from orbit.

To find living organisms, however minute and primitive, on another planet, would bring a new scientific epoch. It would give us our first real hint as to the importance of life itself throughout the universe. Studying it in detail, comparing it to the kinds we

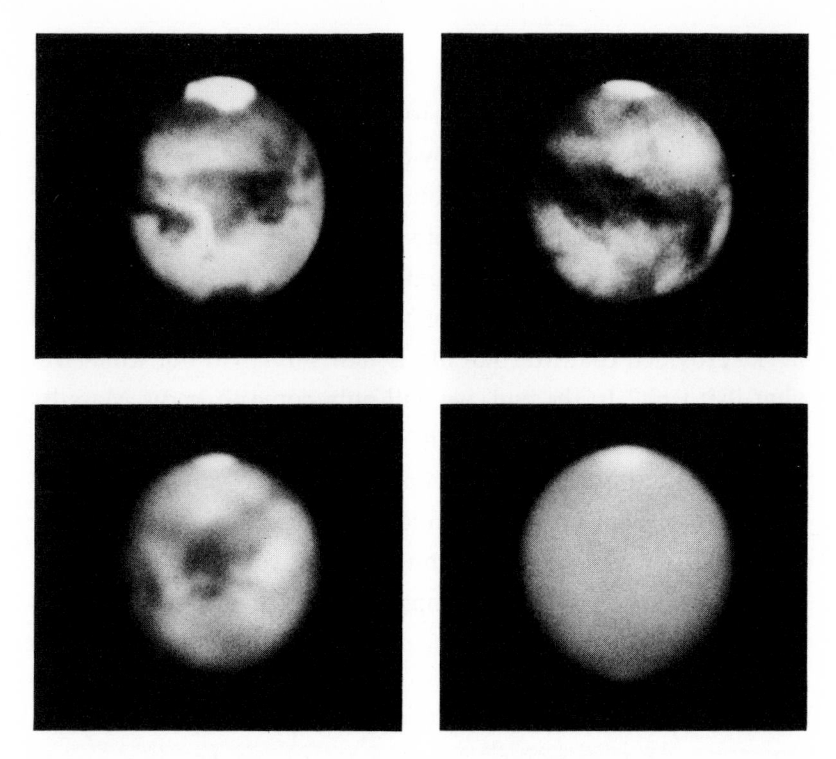

Photographs of Mars taken with a sixty-inch telescope in August and September 1956. The two above show opposite hemispheres. The bulging "ice caps" can be seen at the poles.

know at home, would give us a new biology as superior to the present one as Copernicus' astronomy was to Ptolemy's. What might come of so vastly expanded knowledge, we cannot guess. We are only sure that it would be revolutionary. We dare not hope for intelligent Martians. But microbes will be enough.

If Mars is barren, that is almost as important a piece of information. Although disappointing, it will help us to understand the limits as well as the possibilities of life. However, the planet itself is worth generations of research. It is still more complex and mysterious than the moon, and offers a chance to uncover still other forces of nature.

For such reasons, it calls us. We plan to continue our flybys.

Starting in 1973, NASA hopes to launch a series of more elaborate Voyager probes, boosted by Saturn rockets. There is discussion of landing unmanned vehicles. Among other things, they would test for the presence of life. The testing devices are ingenious. Although somewhat different from each other, in effect they would all look for indications of bacteria in the soil. They should work, provided that Martian life is that similar to our kind. But what if it isn't? In the end, we will only come to know Mars by sending men to explore it on the ground.

NASA has no such project currently under way. Maybe the Russians do. They are making a larger effort in this field than the Americans. At the present writing, they have sent a total of 18 probes to Mars and Venus, compared to our five. Despite several failures, they have learned much, and are frankly interested in doing more.

Whoever launches the first manned expedition, it will probably not consist of a single ship. A fleet of several is more practical, each carrying part of the equipment that will be needed. After taking orbit around Mars, the crews will assemble this gear and some of them will descend in a smaller vehicle.

In the state of our ignorance today, it is hard to describe what those men will experience. We can predict that they will feel lighter in their space armor than on Earth, heavier than on the moon. The sky is dark, with a shrunken sun; the horizon is near. Towering dust clouds sometimes scud past craters that are eroded but mighty. Mountains seemingly exist, though not comparable to Earth's, and so do plains. There are no springs, rivers, lakes, oceans, rain, or snow. Temperature changes are less drastic than on the moon; but the variation between Mars's day and night is like that between Earth's summer and winter.

Otherwise? Who can say? Utter desert, a treasure house only for physical scientists? Or living things as well, or traces of their former existence?

Regardless of the truth, searching it out in detail is vital for the continued advancement of science. It will take a greater, more sustained enterprise than the investigation of the moon. Aside from being remote, Mars is no dwarf. Its area is three times that of North and South America put together. Europeans took centuries to become somewhat familiar with those western continents. They found marvels, and their history took a fresh turn as a result. Will Mars offer us less? It doubtless holds little if any material wealth. But today's source of knowledge, power, and perhaps wisdom is scientific information. In this the planets are rich beyond reckoning.

And just like the moon, Mars should eventually have at least one self-supporting permanent colony. Perhaps this will give rise to others as population grows. People who spend their lives there will come to think of themselves as Martians. They may not set up an independent nation. But they will look on Earth and its affairs with a friendly detachment. From this, their philosophers might conceivably gain insights that will guide mankind toward a better society.

That is sheer speculation, of course. The point is that we cannot foretell the benefits, even the kind of benefits, that may come from an interplanetary age. We will never realize them unless we enter that age boldly, determined to make the best of it.

This means visiting every planet of the Solar System. Venus, next inward, is closer than Mars, and in many ways resembles Earth. The size is only slightly less, though a lower overall density makes the surface gravity about 0.88 of the terrestrial. That serves to hold an extensive atmosphere. It receives nearly twice the solar energy that we do. But the clouds that perpetually hide its surface, and make it shine so beautifully white in our skies, reflect three-fourths of that energy.

Astronomers were always more conservative about Venus than about Mars. This was for the excellent reason that they could observe the red world itself, however indistinctly, through its air. But what could one learn from the featureless veil of

Venus? Writers were free to imagine lush tropical jungles below, oceans that were placid with no moon to raise tides in them, intelligent inhabitants who were savages because they had no chance to see nature's orderliness in heaven like ancient mankind.

Unfortunately for this picturesque image, new methods of research brought new and disheartening facts. The spectroscope showed no trace of oxygen. Radio emanations suggested kilnlike heat. A Mariner passed by and transmitted data that pretty well confirmed it, besides indicating a thicker atmosphere than Earth's.

On October 18, 1967, the Russians scored a dazzling success. The previous year they had crashlanded a probe on Venus. But now they dispatched a vehicle that released a capsule as it swung near the planet. Protected by a heat shield, this 35-inch instrument package, Venera 4, entered the air safely. A parachute opened and it descended, meanwhile radioing its readings to Earth. After 90 minutes it abruptly went silent. But we have not yet finished interpreting the messages that Venera 4 sent us.

Thirty-six hours later, America's Mariner 5 came within 2,480 miles of the surface. It was not intended to land anything. But it did give information that tallied with the Russian data as well as can be expected.

And so we now know that this world's atmosphere is somewhere between 15 and 22 times as dense as Earth's. It is composed mostly of carbon dioxide; the exact percentage may be as low as 75 or as high as 95. There is surprisingly little nitrogen, perhaps 5 percent. A small amount of oxygen was detected, not enough to do humans any good. It is most likely produced by solar energy breaking down water molecules in the upper atmosphere. For a little water vapor does occur near the surface. That indicates the clouds are like Earth's, possibly with some organic or volcanic "smog" lending them their yellowish tinge.

The temperature is appalling. Sixteen miles up, Venera 4 reported 104° F. At cutoff time, near the surface, the reading was 536° F. Quite likely the sizzling heat of the ground put the radio out of commission.

In addition, the two probes confirmed what the earlier Mariner had indicated, that Venus has only a feeble magnetic field, like Mars. The reasons are supposed to be different in the two cases. Apparently planetary magnetism results when rapid rotation sets up currents in a molten core. We believe the masses of Mars and the moon are too slight to squeeze their own central material hard enough to form a core like Earth's. That is, instead of having hot fluid at their centers like our planet, these little worlds are solid rocky balls throughout. Venus is considerably larger, and therefore is believed to have a true core. But it rotates too slowly to create a magnetic field. Radar observations seem to show that its day is equal to 243 of ours, longer than its seven-and-a-half-month year. Strangely, this turning is not from west to east, like that of every other planet and most moons that we know about. Venus spins in the opposite direction.

We thus picture the landscape as a gloomy waste of raw rock. Some minerals may be molten, but generally the terrain is hard and searingly hot. There are probably mountains, some very high; but no snows crown them, no cataracts rush down their flanks, no forests clothe their foothills. All water, except for the merest trace of vapor, has risen to altitudes where the temperature is low and condensed into cloud. The poisonous air is quiet, too heavy for quick breezes or cleansing stormwinds. Perhaps banks and tendrils of ill-colored chemical compounds drift slowly along—but no life, not until men arrive.

For though the planet looks hellish, and will certainly be difficult and dangerous to explore, we cannot stay away. Venus poses too many riddles. We will not be sure that our theories about it

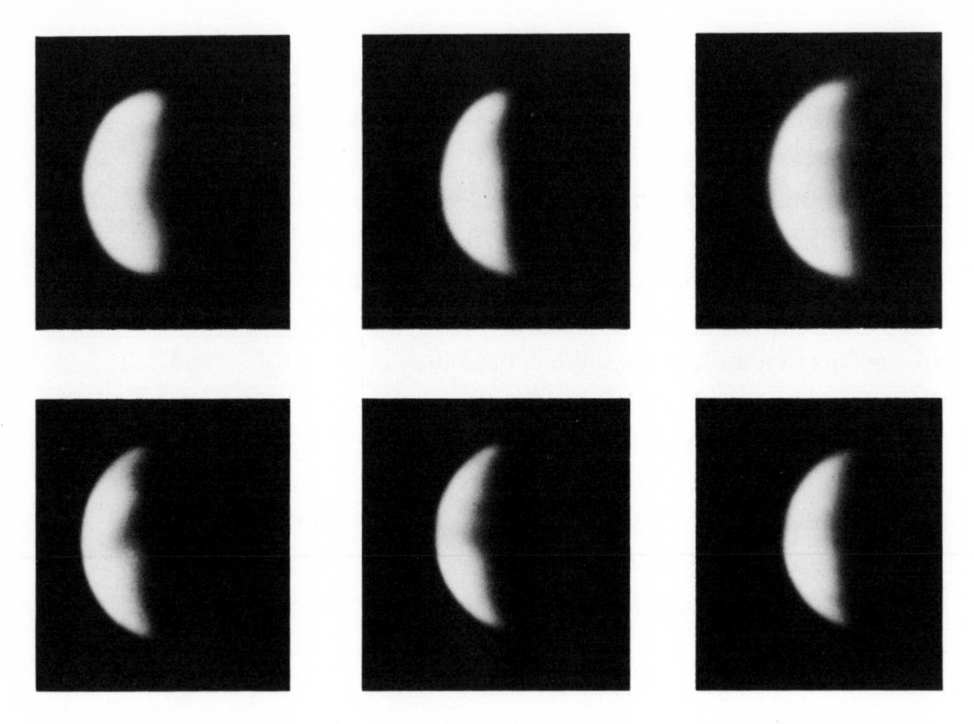

Shrouded in clouds, Venus rotates slowly from east to west, its day longer than its year.

are correct until we have visited the reality. We do not have any absolute assurance that the world is barren. Microbial life might drift in the cool clouds. Or something totally alien, in its basic chemistry as well as its shape, may walk upon that scorching soil and grow upward into that furnace air. Far more than an inhabited Mars, an inhabited Venus would expand our horizons.

Granting that this is extremely unlikely, we nevertheless have much to find out. Why does the planet rotate so slowly, and backward? Some have suggested it is due to the tidal action of the nearby sun on the thick atmosphere. But in the present state of our knowledge, that is a mere guess. What causes a temperature so much higher than we expected? Does the air, with its peculiar composition, trap heat? Is the solid body itself hot by nature? Why has Venus, akin to Earth in so many respects, kept that enormous volume of gas? What chemistry, geology, and weather exist there? Once more, the questions are endless, and strike at the foundations of our understanding of the universe. Only manned expeditions can answer most of them, especially the supreme one: What complete surprises does Venus have for us?

No doubt the first several ships will just send down unmanned probes from their orbits. On the basis of what these reveal, engineers can design proper vehicles for men. Those might include insulated, refrigerated tanks for driving about, aircraft for flying. Whether or not a permanent colony on Venus would be worthwhile is hard to say. The cost, effort, and danger may be too great. Or they may not be. It is very likely that, fifty or a hundred years from now, men will do with ease what we today cannot do at all.

They might at last perform the godlike feat of making the planet come alive. Dr. Sagan has suggested one theoretically possible means. Certain types of algae thrive at elevated temperatures. Like other photosynthetic plants, they consume carbon dioxide and release oxygen. Venus might be a paradise for them. Floating in the air, with no natural enemies, they would fill it practically overnight. As the atmospheric composition changes, temperature ought to drop, until the clouds break up in a gigantic rain. The process involves numerous technicalities, and if it can be carried out, it requires a huge enterprise. But the end result could be that mild, fertile, rich, wholly livable world about which we once daydreamed.

A new earth would repay everything that every generation had invested in space, a thousand times over.

Dr. Sagan made it plain that his idea may never be realizable. Once again we must apply what seems to be a good motto for the space age: "You don't know till you've been there!" At the absolute least, Venus has more to give us than we now imagine.

CHAPTER 9

Sister Planets

We shall have less to say about each of the remaining worlds in the Solar System. That is not because they are less interesting but because we are more ignorant about them. Every planet is unique, with special things to teach us. But we will only learn the details when men search them out in person.

The fourth nearest globe—after the moon, Venus, and Mars—is Mercury. But it may not be visited, except by probes and robots, before human feet have trod more distant ones. The obstacles are large. Closest to the sun, at an average distance of 36 million miles, it receives 17 times the radiation that we do. Instruments have recorded temperatures on the daylit side as high as 770° F., sufficient to melt lead. Nor is there a thick air blanket, and probably there is no magnetic field, to screen out the deadly parts of the sun's energy. For Mercury is a bare 3,100 miles in diameter, its mass only 5 percent of Earth's and its surface gravity about one-third g.

Nevertheless, this pygmy is already astonishing us. For a long time astronomers took for granted that the early observers were right when they declared that Mercury rotates once in its eighty-eight-day year. Thus it always turned the same face to the sun. Our moon behaves similarly with respect to us. The reason lies in the tidal pull of Earth upon it. Deep in the solar gravitational field, Mercury must be affected in the same way. One hemisphere was said to lie in eternal heat, the other in darkness and a cold near absolute zero. No atmosphere was left, except for what gases might have frozen on the night side.

Within the past few years, this picture has been shattered. Direct measurement of temperature on the unlighted hemisphere is difficult, since it does not radiate very strongly. But modern electronic instruments accomplished the task and showed that the nighted half of Mercury is not cold at all. Instead, it is at approximately room temperature. This seemed impossible without air to carry warmth, and close investigation did reveal a wispy atmosphere. Meanwhile, radar data showed that the real rotation period is about fifty-eight days. Mathematical papers appeared soon after to prove that the Mercurian day should indeed be equal to two-thirds of the year. Hindsight is always keener than foresight.

Innumerable mysteries remain. To name only one, what about the atmosphere? What is it composed of, how dense is it, how can it be in the first place?

Mercury is scarcely a pleasant location for humans, except to the extent that adventure, discovery, and achievement give pleasure. When ships come, better shielded and screened than any we can build today, the crews will doubtless be sheltered underground or in a cave. Perhaps they will never venture out by day. We believe the landscape resembles the moon's, though more eroded. The air must be poisonous to us, and unbreathably thin in any case, maybe so thin that unaided ears cannot hear the winds that blow across those harsh miles. Yet, men will revel in the excitement of being on a whole new world.

We cannot predict what they will find. Life is imaginable on Mercury. It could consist of microbes like those we have suggested might populate the moon. Larger forms cannot be flatly ruled out. Creatures may exist that are absolutely alien, not built of proteins like us but of something more hardy. For example, the famous science writer Isaac Asimov has played with the idea of a life chemistry that uses atoms of fluorine where ours uses hydrogen, and molten sulfur instead of water. Its material would not be destroyed by the heat of Venus or the Mercurian day.

Dr. Asimov, like Dr. Sagan, warns that such thoughts may be dead wrong. But when little Mercury overturns our most solid-seeming theories, we cannot very well use other theories to set absolute limits on what nature can do.

Turning from the sun, starward, we come upon the asteroids. Most of these bodies orbit between Mars and Jupiter, though a few come farther in or go farther out. Over 1,500 have been identified, and new ones turn up every year. They are generally tiny, "flying mountains" or less. The largest, Ceres, does have a diameter of 480 miles, but most are not comparable. Thousands must be meteoroids, too small to detect from Earth.

Frigid, airless, waterless, almost certainly lifeless, the asteroids once seemed quite uninteresting. They will be no menace to spaceships. Their orbits are so enormous—250 million miles from the sun is typical—that they are scattered across truly astronomical distances. It will be rare for travelers to pick one up on radar, let alone see it pass by.

Today we have many reasons for wishing to visit the asteroids. They are worth studying for their own sake, for the records of cosmic radiation that they preserve in their crystal structures, and for the clues they will give to the beginnings of the Solar System. Have they always been as they are? If so, why? Are they the debris of a planet that exploded? If so, how? Consider how much information we have gotten from meteorites on Earth and you will see what scientific riches are in the asteroids.

In time they may become more. They may surpass the moon in giving man dominion over space. For though they are small, they are numerous. Besides, an object several miles thick is not to be ignored. The total mineral wealth is incredible, and should be easier to get at than on the moon or on a planet. There is less overlying mass to dig through. We can guess that useful and valuable materials are often right on the surface.

Asteroid gravity is feeble, less than 1 percent of g for Ceres, lower yet for the others. Scant power is necessary to boost a cargo free of that. Prospectors could mount engines directly on the minor ones and fly them to an orbital processing plant. Solar radiation is weakened by distance, far less dangerous than on the moon. At the same time, sunlight is bright enough for easy vision. We have already remarked that it is not difficult to keep warm in a ship, a suit, or a dwelling that is properly designed for space.

We can imagine whole cities created in the asteroid belt. Each is biologically self-supporting. There generations of people live out their lives. They prefer the freedom of flitting between worldlets to the heavy weight and tame routines of Earth. An energetic spaceborne civilization develops, exporting metals to the whole Solar System, building its own ships and conducting its own explorations. With that kind of tradition and resources, the "asterites" may be the first humans to go to the stars.

Once again we are describing something that may never come to pass. But it does remind us how many wonders the space age holds in store, most of them undreamed of today.

Some thinkers believe that meteoroids are, at least in part, the remnants of disintegrated comets. The idea is that these wanderers originate in the farthest reaches of the Solar System as clumps of gravel and boulders held together by frozen gases. Moving slowly inward on its tremendous orbit, a comet at length comes near the sun and warms up. Evaporating, pushed out by light pressure, the gas forms a glowing head and tail. Having low mass, comets are readily pulled into new and shorter orbits by the planets. This spells their doom, for each time they approach the sun they lose more of their substance. In the end, nothing remains but a cluster of stones.

We would naturally like to know if this theory is right. And it leaves numerous questions unanswered, such as the way in which comets were formed. They must preserve gases from the very earliest ages. To dig down through these layers and analyze samples would be to cast new light on the nature of the universe.

Hence, a rendezvous with a comet will be more than an exciting adventure. It will be a triumph for the progress of knowledge.

Four hundred and eighty-three million miles from the sun, 317 times as massive as Earth, is Jupiter, the king planet of the Solar System. Nine known moons swing around it, two of them larger than Mercury. Through a telescope, the disc glows tawny, banded with colored clouds that are longer than our own globe is wide. The Great Red Spot, a marking whose nature is unknown, reaches across 30,000 miles. The diameter of Jupiter is 88,700 miles at the equator. A rapid rotation, once in slightly less than 10 hours, has flattened the sphere until the distance from pole to pole is 4,900 miles less. Given these figures, we can calculate that the surface gravity is about 2.5 g. A man who weighed 200 pounds at home would weigh 600 pounds or more there. The measured temperature is around 200 Fahrenheit degrees below zero.

What we observe is not necessarily what an imaginary native

Ganymede, one of the nine moons of Jupiter, casts its shadow near the Great Red Spot. Thirty thousand miles wide, the Spot's nature is unknown.

of Jupiter would experience. The atmosphere is vast and cloudy; we do not see past the uppermost layers. Farther down, gravity must be higher still. Air pressure on the Jovian surface is probably greater than at the bottom of the terrestrial oceans. (This is supposing that Jupiter has a definite surface like the inner worlds. Some authorities maintain that the gas simply gets denser and denser until pressure causes it to collapse into a different form of matter.) The spectroscope reveals the poisons methane and ammonia in that atmosphere, plus traces of other compounds. But we believe it is mainly hydrogen and helium.

Although the distant sun shines with only one twenty-seventh the intensity that it does on man's home, Jupiter is surrounded by Van Allen radiation belts, bigger than ours. They are due to its immense magnetic field, which traps charged particles. Spiraling, these particles give off radiation of their own. The planet itself emits strong radio waves. Their source is presumably electric storms, many of which could swallow Earth whole; but we are not certain.

Altogether, Jupiter is in its way the most marvelous and mysterious member of the Solar System. Unraveling its secrets, we will come upon conditions and events that occur nowhere else. This, in turn, will confer new knowledge and capabilities on us. Scientists look forward eagerly to the sending of Mariner-like probes. But someday men will have to go.

No matter how powerful their spaceship, they will not land on the planet. If a wind did not wreck the vessel first, the atmosphere would crumple it as it descended. However, the satellites offer good sites for scientific bases. From the bleak lands of Ganymede, the largest, Jupiter shows 15 times as wide as the full moon seen from Earth, 52 times as bright. Little inmost Amalthea is just 112,600 miles from its master, which thus appears 92 times as broad as our moon. That sky-filling spectacle of colors, clouds, whirlpool turbulences, lightnings, auroras, must be one of the most beautiful as well as stupefying sights in the universe.

Once established on the satellites, men can study Jupiter at short range with instruments and unmanned vehicles. They are bound to make many astounding discoveries. It may prove to be true what Carl Sagan has suggested, that the planet is not frozen. The low temperatures we have measured are in the upper atmosphere, which is cold on Earth too. Various gases trap heat. They include carbon dioxide and water vapor; without them, our globe would be much chillier than it is. They also include methane and ammonia, which Jupiter possesses in abundance. So perhaps its hypothetical surface is fairly warm, conceivably as warm as Earth's.

Could life arise? The question is not an idle one. We know the Jovian atmosphere contains organic compounds that we think were forerunners of life here and that continue to be associated with it. While sunlight cannot struggle through hundreds of miles of murky air, higher levels might contain floating plankton-like organisms. Farther down, the energy of sunlight is indirectly present in such forms as lightning. Given that complex environment, things could happen that are impossible elsewhere. True, the life would be different from ours in most respects. Yet, it need not be as different as it would have to be on Mercury or Venus.

To solve these and other riddles, manned expeditions to Jupiter might at last take place. They demand a special kind of ship, one that can withstand the terrible conditions. A two-mode vessel could be designed for the purpose. One part uses rocket thrust to leave the satellite or orbital base and enter the Jovian atmosphere (as well as to return afterward). Then the other part takes over, using jets or airscrews for motion and a dirigible structure for support. The men and their gear are in a single, immensely thick-walled unit that will not be crushed. In short,

The rings of Saturn may be orbiting ice crystals. At 886 million miles from the Sun, Saturn receives 1 per cent of the light Earth does.

the craft operates on the same principle as the bathyscaphe does visiting terrestrial ocean depths.

We cannot do this today, and perhaps man will never be able to. But I think it more likely that he will, if he cares to make the effort. The rewards of success are incalculable.

Beyond Jupiter we find three more planets of majestic size—Saturn, Uranus, and Neptune. At 886 million miles from the sun, Saturn gets only about 1 percent of the light that we do. And in spite of its extensive atmosphere, with methane and ammonia, it seems a poor candidate for life. But we cannot be sure.

Our information is sparse about this world. Its fascinating rings appear to be orbiting ice crystals. But what made them? The largest of its ten moons, Titan, exceeds Ganymede in bulk, has thin air and is well worth investigation.

Uranus, which is 1,782,800,000 miles out, spins on a wildly tilted axis. Neptune's distance of 2,793,500,000 miles is impressive, to say the least; but it is less than it should be according to a mathematical rule that governs the positioning of every other planet. Pluto, at 3,675,000,000 miles on the average, is roughly where Neptune ought to be, and many astronomers think this smallish world is an escaped Neptunian satellite. But Pluto's orbit is the one most slanted with respect to all others. Barring comets and a few asteroids, it is the most eccentric, too. At times, in its period of 248 years, Pluto comes nearer to the sun than Neptune.

Something very strange seems to have happened in those remote marchlands of the Solar System. And there are endlessly more questions, including those we do not yet know enough to ask. The farthest, darkest, coldest worlds call the explorers of tomorrow with a challenge and a promise.

CHAPTER

10

More Suns Than One

Our look at our neighborhood in space has been far too brief. We have mentioned only a few of the possibilities and the mysteries within the sun's realm. They will keep us busy for much longer than the next fifty years. If we never get any farther than Pluto, we have many centuries of adventure and accomplishment ahead of us.

Nevertheless, already our thoughts go toward the stars.

We know that those points of light that glitter across the sky after dark are actually other suns. Not all of them resemble our own. Most of those that we see are vastly larger and brighter, like red Betelgeuse with 1,200 times the solar radiance, or blue-white Canopus with 80,000. The reason for this is not that such giants are common. They are, in truth, comparatively rare. But most stars are so far away that the naked eye cannot pick out any except the greatest.

A handy unit for expressing these distances is the light-year. It is the span that light covers in one year, traveling through space at better than 186,000 miles per second; it equals approximately six million million miles. If we were 56 light-years from our sun, we would no longer be able to see it without a telescope. But the giants are visible across hundreds of light-years.

Instruments give us a more balanced picture. They show that, as a rule, the less luminous a kind of star is, the commoner it is. The brightness depends on a number of factors, but especially on mass. A very brilliant star is also usually a very massive one. It is so hot that its overall color is bluish or whitish. The atomic reactions that power it take place extremely fast, because the tremendous pressure at the center squeezes atoms together so hard. Being an energy spendthrift, a blue star does not live long. After some millions of years, it has exhausted its resources. It flares up, producing what is called a supernova, momentarily equal to millions or even billions of ordinary stars. Then it quickly dwindles away.

The lesser orbs like Sol are cooler, hence yellowish in hue. Their glow is more modest and they live correspondingly longer. Astronomers believe that our sun is about five billion years old and will continue in its present style for an equal length of time. Then it too must die. But instead of exploding, it will gradually swell, until its bloated body has engulfed the inner planets. During this time, the total output of heat and light will increase. But because that energy must pass through a mass spread thin and a surface spread wide, the outside temperature will drop. Therefore Sol will become a red giant, fairly similar to Betelgeuse now. Afterward it will collapse, waxing and waning like a guttering fire, but always shining more feebly until the last gleam vanishes. With five billion years ahead of us, we need not worry about this!

Smaller suns than ours are more numerous yet, until we reach the red dwarfs. These occur ten times as frequently as the solar type. They have roughly one-half the mass and give off 1 percent or less of the energy. By way of compensation, their life spans are enormous, as long as one hundred billion years.

These are just the principal kinds of stars. We know others. Some are variable, brighter at one time than at another. Some are "white dwarfs," dim, no bigger than a planet, but so compressed that a teaspoonful of their matter amounts to a ton or more. Some are misty thin. Some are surrounded by haze. Some sport colorful rings of hydrogen gas. Some emit gigantic flares, as big as themselves. Most of these are old and waning. But we have lately identified others that are being born, condensing out of interstellar dust and gas. The Orion Nebula is one place where this is happening.

Many scientists think there may be objects smaller than the red dwarfs, too small to shine. Below a certain mass, atomic reactions cannot start of themselves within a body. The pressure is not high enough. That is why planets are not luminous like stars. So far no one has managed to detect a "black dwarf."

A great many stars, perhaps a majority, occur in pairs, orbiting around each other at various distances. Triplets also exist, quadruplets, and so on, up to gigantic clusters of millions.

All these, plus types that we have not mentioned, belong to the galaxy. This is a stellar association whose grandeur strikes every thoughtful person with wonder. Seen from the edge, it is lens-shaped, 6,500 light-years thick at the center and 100,000 light-years across. From "above," it looks like a pinwheel, with two spiral arms coiling outward. It contains at least 100 billion individual suns. But its size is such that their average separation is a matter of light-years—about 8 or 9 in our vicinity. (To be sure, we are far out in one arm, 30,000 light-years from the center, where the stars are sparse. But even in the crowded heart,

The "Horsehead" Nebula in Orion.

they probably seldom come within a light-year of each other. We cannot be certain, because that middle region is hidden from us by immense interstellar clouds.)

Our galaxy is not the whole universe. On the contrary! We have photographed billions of galaxies, and do not know how many there are altogether. Maybe their number is infinite. The closest of them are the Magellanic Clouds, an irregularly shaped pair that lie some 165,000 light-years off. They are only visible from our southern hemisphere. Northerners can see the next nearest in the constellation Andromeda, across a million and a half light-years. To the eye, it is a dim, fuzzy patch of glow. Telescopes and cameras show it to be as big and intricate as our own.

Astronomy is one of man's noblest endeavors. The cosmos that it reveals to us is more beautiful and inspiring, as well as larger than Ptolemy's. Yet, we cannot deny that it seems a lonely place. Are we the sole creatures in all that expanse who look upon it, think, and marvel? If not, will we ever know that we have spiritual kin out there? How can we bridge the abysses between us and them? The answer is one to stun us. We may make contact with beings who live beneath foreign suns—and not in some remote future, but in our personal lifetimes!

This is not guaranteed. Rather, the chances are somewhat against it. But most of the scientists who have given serious thought to the subject believe that the odds are not hopelessly bad, provided we make the necessary effort. And, while it *is* a gamble, the risk is slight. Should we win, the rewards could exceed our wildest imaginings.

What is the likelihood of anyone, or anything, being alive off Earth? As we have said, the fellow planets of the Solar System do not look very promising, with the possible exceptions of Mars and Jupiter. Whatever life they contain, if any, is probably not intelligent.

We will not be sure until we have explored. And then we may

not instantly recognize thinking creatures for what they are. A controversy is going on today as to whether or not dolphins compare to men in brain power. Dolphins are warm-blooded oxygen breathers like us, living on the same globe, descended from a common ancestor. A Martian or a Jovian might think and act so differently from a human visitor that neither party guesses the other is anything but a peculiar animal.

Let us be conservative, though, and suppose that Earth is the single inhabited world in the Solar System. Let us further suppose that life can only arise from the original raw chemicals on planets that are more or less like Earth. We have no proof that this is true. But we do have good reason to believe that on any world that resembles this one at its own beginnings, a life chemistry will develop that is fairly similar to ours; and eventually, thanks largely to photosynthesis, the atmosphere will have abundant free oxygen.

The question is, therefore, how many such worlds exist. Astronomers believe today that most stars have planets. Theory suggests it. Apparently the sun and its family condensed from a cosmic cloud. If that is right, then this is a normal sort of event that happens repeatedly.

Observation bears out the idea. No planet of another sun has been found by telescope. Perhaps in the future a space observatory will succeed, but not one that is handicapped by being on Earth. Meanwhile, though, the slow spin of ordinary stars, in contrast to giants, makes it look reasonable that the former have companions. And lately an attendant of Barnard's Star was discovered, by its effect on the motion of that red dwarf. It has half again the mass of Jupiter, which makes it definitely a planet, not a tiny sun. The coincidence would be fantastic if Sol and Barnard's Star were the only cases.

Granted that planets are common, we must next ask if life is. What are the requirements? First is the right kind of sun. As we

There are billions of galaxies in the universe. Shown, the Spiral Galaxy in Pisces.

have seen, the blue giants are short-lived, while several other types, such as the red giants and white dwarfs, are dying. But the large majority of known stars are in a healthy, stable condition.

The red dwarfs may be too cool. The astronomer Su-Shu Huang thinks so. He argues that it is most unlikely that any of them has a planet at exactly the right distance, where water neither boils nor freezes. This range is less narrow for brighter stars like Sol, just as the range of comfortable temperature is less narrow around a big campfire than a little one. Therefore, the yellow and orange stars have a better chance of a world or two in the proper zone than do the red stars. We have seen that the dim dwarfs greatly outnumber suns like ours.

Likewise, Dr. Huang declares, the star must be a single one. A companion would disturb the orbits of any planets too much. This rules out at least half the remaining possibilities.

On these grounds, he admits only two that are worth thinking about in this immediate region, Epsilon Eridani and Tau Ceti. Both are about one-third as luminous as Sol and lie, in separate directions, at distances of roughly 11 and 12 light-years, respectively. Throughout the universe as a whole, Dr. Huang thinks, 3 to 5 percent of the stars have a life-bearing planet each.

His estimate gives us several billion inhabited worlds in our galaxy alone. Most of them are extremely distant. But within 50 light-years of us are some hundred stars not too unlike Sol. Therefore, this cautious attitude allows us a good chance of extraterrestrial life inside that radius.

Other authorities are more optimistic. They point out that we have already detected planets of a few double stars, again by their gravitational effects. These are monsters, from 10 to 16 times as massive as Jupiter. But they do indicate that Earth-sized bodies can exist in such a system, if only as satellites of themselves.

And perhaps a world of a red dwarf can have a comfortable

temperature. For instance, it might possess a denser and more heat-trapping atmosphere than Earth, as Venus does.

This kind of reasoning can be used to support the guess that at least half the stars have at least one planet apiece on which there is life. That would mean 50 billion or better in the galaxy, and thousands within 50 or 100 light-years of us. Whether this view is correct, or the pessimistic one is, or some in-between estimate, we do not know.

Nor do we know if life necessarily produces intelligence, or intelligence necessarily produces civilization. We have precisely one case available to study, ourselves. Maybe the universe is populated chiefly by unthinking plants and animals. Maybe the thinking beings are mostly savages, and always will be. But it is more reasonable to suppose that we are not unique. We are not radically different from the other higher mammals on Earth. Nor is Earth radically different from the other inner planets of the Solar System, nor is Sol in any way an extraordinary star. The most conservative guess is that we are about average in the cosmos.

This does not mean that natives of remote worlds look or act like us. The chances are that they don't. Their evolution has been unrelated to ours from the very first. They may well have made similar adaptations to similar environments. For instance, they are more apt to be warm-blooded, and have bones inside their bodies, than they are to be giant insects. But the peculiarities of detail could be endless.

So when we say that man is probably about average, we mean that he would not stand out especially among the many types of planetarians that exist, could they all be gathered together. The same holds good for man's ways of living and thinking, and for his present stage of development. We would be as exotic to another race as it would be to us.

To make contact with such beings would be one of the most

exciting and rewarding events in the whole of history. How could communication be established?

At once we think of radio. Given suitable instruments, especially if they are mounted in space, radio can be detected at great distances. In the past fifty years or so, broadcasting has made Earth the second most powerful radio source in the Solar System, next to the sun. If there are any observers with the appropriate equipment within several light-years, they have noticed this sudden change already.

For true interstellar communication, however, we need something more specialized. This might be, not a broadcast, but a beam of microwave radio on a suitable band. Given a powerful transmitter, it would travel very far indeed before sinking into oblivion. The electronics expert Bernard Oliver has proposed a design for a large and supersensitive radio telescope. If it were built, it could receive ultra-high-frequency television at 200 light-years, an Aero-Ciba space radar at 1,400, and "Haystack" radar beams at 15,000!

We have made extensive use of radio for a bare half century. It would be strange if the galaxy does not contain civilizations that began earlier and are further along than man. Today we talk about contacting them. Could they already be trying to get in touch with us? They may or may not know that we are here. Probably they don't. But they could beam signals anyway, hoping for a reply.

In 1959, the physicists Giuseppe Cocconi and Philip Morrison proposed that we use our big radio telescopes on a part-time basis to listen for interstellar calls. They suggested plausible wavelengths. Under the direction of Frank Drake, the United States National Radio Astronomy Observatory actually made the attempt. Project Ozma, as it was named, focused on Epsilon Eridani and Tau Ceti. It received nothing except natural and man-made noise. But these are only two stars out of untold numbers. And the aliens are not bound to choose the means that we would. They might employ a different radio band, or lasers, or something else, perhaps something that we are not yet able to detect.

If we do one day receive a signal, what will it be like? It will scarcely use any language of Earth. But it might well go through a series of mathematical relationships. We could identify statements like "$2 + 2 = 4$." This would give us symbols for arithmetic, from which we could proceed to more complicated ideas. Dr. Drake worked out a message which was nothing but a long series of ones and zeroes, and asked his friends to decode it. Most of them succeeded. It turned out to describe a set of points that formed pictures of nonhuman beings, their planetary system, and so forth. Other thinkers have amused themselves by working out complete radio-code languages that listeners could readily learn.

In order to reply, we would have to build special apparatus. But as Dr. Oliver's work shows, this is simply a matter of determination. We could also probe the sky with messages of our own. A good place for that transmitter would be the far side of the moon, where there is no radio interference from Earth. The station could be automated and sun-powered, patiently sending to star after star, decade after decade, until at last it flashed the news that something was coming in.

Imagine that contact has been made. Since light takes 4.3 years to go from here to the nearest star, Alpha Centauri, a message would too. Almost nine years must elapse between question and answer. And the chances are that we shall have to beam farther. If the distance is 50 light-years, a man who helps prepare a transmission will not live to see the response to it.

Nevertheless, this exchange would be supremely worthwhile. It would hardly be a simple dialogue. Rather, each party would transmit continuously. As a mutual language developed, they would convey information that was more and more subtle. But even in the early stages, they would have unbelievably much to tell each other.

Think how important it would be to science to get a complete description of a planet in another system and the life on it. Think what discoveries and inventions the aliens might have made that have never occurred to us. Remembering how profoundly different cultures here on Earth have influenced each other, think what insights we might gain from nonhuman history, religion, philosophy, arts, and customs.

The same should apply to those dwellers on distant worlds. Perhaps the galaxy is already crisscrossed with messages and we are latecomers. Or perhaps a civilization in range of us is waiting to hear from someone else before it starts sending.

We will not know until we have tried both to listen and to call. This we can do almost incidentally, in the course of the new interplanetary age. What we learn could change our entire destiny for the better.

CHAPTER 11

Voyage to the Stars

Although we may talk with other worlds, across light-years and centuries, will we ever visit them?

Most scientists think not. The stars are too far. Traveling at a thousand miles a second, we would take 800 years to reach Alpha Centauri. And this multiple system lies closer to Sol than the normal distance between local suns.

But we have described high-powered ion drives of the future that will push spacecraft to large velocities. Why not accelerate to a hundred million miles per second and make the crossing in a few hours?

Nature raises two basic objections to that. First, even at one g, it takes almost a year to reach the speed of light, 186,000 miles per second. We do not know how much added weight humans can tolerate for a long period, but the limit is doubtless somewhere under three g. Accordingly, at best an interstellar voyage will not be short.

Second, it appears to be impossible to travel faster than light. The reason is not too hard to understand. As Einstein's theory of relativity shows, energy and mass are interchangeable. It is on this basis that we get atomic power, changing a little of the matter in our fuel or explosive into pure radiant energy. We can also do the reverse thing on a small scale, forcing a unit of X-ray energy to become a pair of electrons, one negatively charged and one positively.

The faster a body moves, the more energy it has, and thus the more massive it becomes. This means that more energy is needed to add one mile per second to a high speed than is needed to increase a low speed by that same amount. The difference is not noticeable in ordinary life, but at extremely large velocities it begins to show up to a greater and greater degree. The equations, and practical experience with nuclear physics, prove that the energy required to accelerate a material object up to just the speed of light is infinite.

This means that that speed is unreachable by anything except light itself. No matter how much power you apply, whether to a single atom or an entire spaceship, it will not be enough. You can come very close to light velocity, perhaps, but you can never quite reach it.

So, while scientists often enjoy science fiction stories, they doubt if any ship, in all time to come, will zoom across the galaxy quickly and easily.

They could be wrong. Maybe we will discover some new principle of physics by which we can evade nature's speed limit and cushion astronauts against high accelerations. This is what science fiction terms like "warp factor" imply. But at present, no such possibility is known to us. On that account, many authorities believe we will always remain within the Solar System.

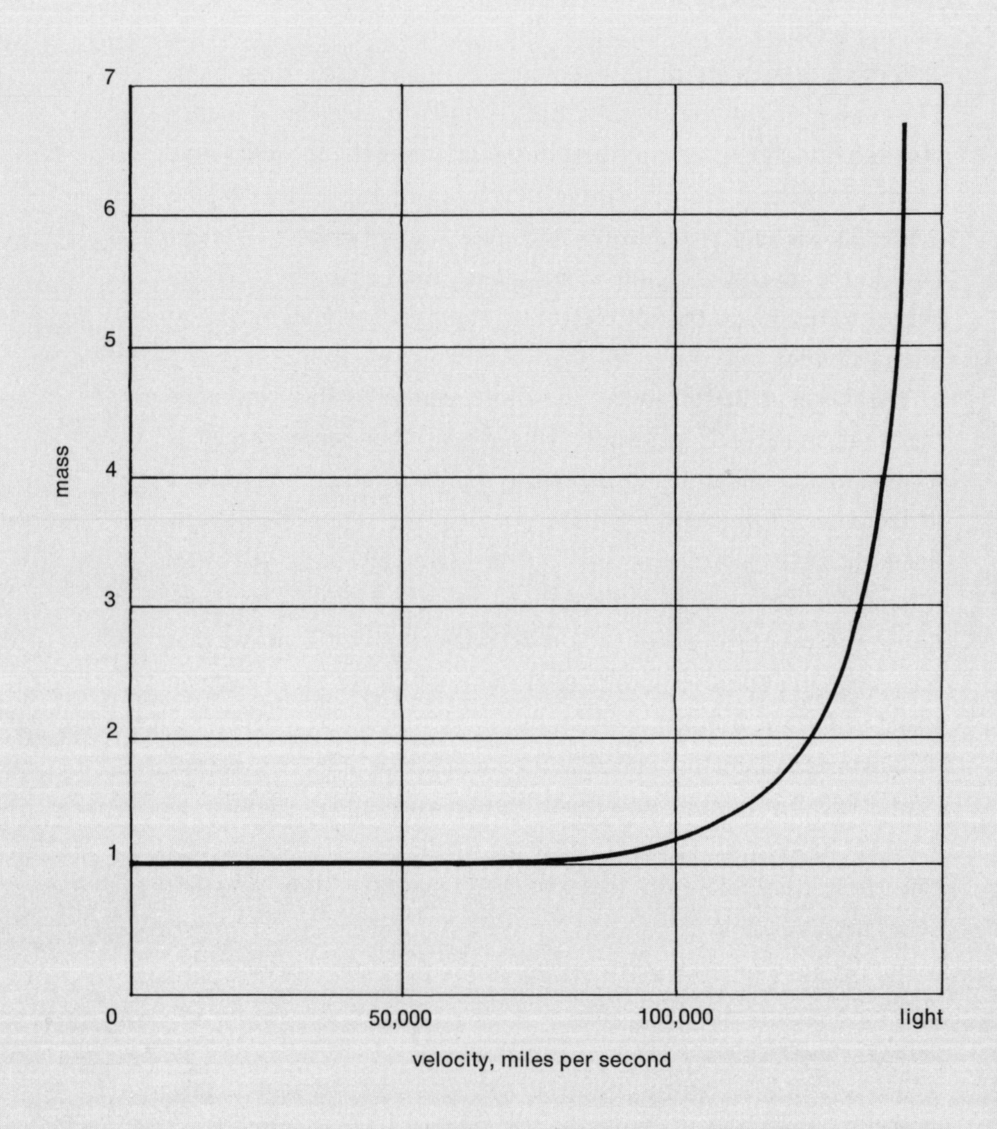

The faster a body moves, the more energy—and mass—it has.

Other experts are convinced that our descendants *can* reach the stars, regardless of relativity. The undertaking is difficult, they say, but not unthinkable.

If necessary, ships could take centuries for a passage. The crews could lie in suspended animation meanwhile. We cannot today put humans in a state where they will rest, unconscious, not aging, until the time when a machine revives them. Several lines of research suggest, however, that we will find ways to do this in the future.

If not, we could build exceedingly large vessels, biologically self-supporting like space stations. Men and women could travel together in them, marry and raise children. After generations had passed, the people that were then alive would approach their goal.

In either case, the crews would return to an Earth that they scarcely recognized. Hundreds of years of history would have passed. The very nations that sent the star ships forth might no longer exist. The travelers would feel themselves utter strangers.

Then why take the trouble?

The reasons are the same as the reasons for sending men to the planets of the Solar System, but even stronger. No doubt instrumented probes will go first, and beam back word of what they find. Yet, we have seen how limited a machine is. And we have also seen how valuable it will be to obtain complete information about any other world. This is doubly true of the worlds that circle other stars, since we cannot observe them directly from here. And it is triply true of a planet that has intelligent natives.

Whatever radio contacts we may make with beings outside the Solar System, there must be more races that do not have radio or do not choose to send messages. They are every bit as interesting, and may well have much to teach us. Consider what European man learned from the arts of Africa and the agriculture of the American Indian, not to mention the ancient civilizations of the Orient and his own pre-electronic ancestors.

For these reasons, as well as the sheer adventure, people should not be lacking who will make the journeys. Those who return may come as foreigners to their own changed planet; but it will welcome them as heroes. Or if they find a congenial globe beneath another sun, they may colonize it and beam their findings back. The chance of winning an entire new earth, belonging to no natives but full of life, should lure many a person starward.

Besides, long crossings may well be avoidable. If we can travel near the speed of light, the time between stars shrinks to years rather than centuries. For example, here is an approximate timetable for a voyage to the star Tau Ceti. You will recall that it is not unlike Sol and about 12 light-years distant.

We accelerate at one g for one year (355 days, to be exact) to reach almost the ultimate velocity. In that time we cover half a light-year. Now we must conserve fuel, so we switch off the engines, spin the big hull to furnish weight, and settle down. In obedience to Newton's first law, the ship continues in a nearly straight line at a nearly unchanging speed for 11 years. Then we apply reverse thrust at one g, backing down upon our destination, for one more year. When we arrive, 13 years have elapsed.

We put our vessel in orbit and use smaller auxiliary craft for landing on the planets of Tau Ceti. To make the trip worthwhile, we spend 10 years exploring. Besides, we are having too much fun to stop. But in the end, we return. Our flight pattern homeward is like the pattern outward, requiring 13 years. We reach Earth 36 years after we departed it. That is not such a great lapse of time. We should be able to fit ourselves back into everyday life without undue difficulty.

Have we not, though, grown quite old?

No. For us, the time has been only about 14 years!

This paradox arises from the same laws of relativity that set a light-speed restriction on our traveling. When two bodies move at different velocities, time passes at different rates for them. Ordinarily this difference is too slight to measure, just as in the case of changes in mass. But as we come near to light speed, the time factor becomes greater and greater. It approaches zero as a limit. If we traveled exactly as fast as light, we could cross a million light-years in no time at all, as far as we were concerned. (Of course, someone who stayed put would measure the time of our passage as a million years.) This is impossible. But in theory, at least, we can come close to achieving it.

Aboard a very fast-moving spaceship, we would not feel anything unusual. We would see the outside cosmos as having an altered time rate, not us. The sky would become very strange; colors and positions, even shapes and masses of the stars would be other than what we were used to. As we slowed down, everything would begin to look normal once more.

Therefore, the twenty-two years of moving near light speed, to and from Tau Ceti, hardly count. Only the total of four years' acceleration, plus the time spent at the target sun, are important.

The longer the voyage, the smaller those four years loom in proportion. Traveling a thousand light-years and back would scarcely age us more than a trip to a nearby star would. Admittedly, meanwhile everything else would experience time at the normal rate.

Returning to Earth after two thousand years might make us like someone from the era of Christ, lifted suddenly into the twentieth century. In spite of all social difficulties, a time traveler would be royally welcomed for what he could tell us. In the same way, star travelers ought to be received with joy when they come home. No doubt special educational techniques will be developed for bringing them rapidly up to date.

Many scientists say of this idea, "Well, it is theoretically all right. But it will never be done in practice. You'd need more power than you could generate or handle. Anyhow, the radiation would kill you." Perhaps they are right. But others disagree.

Looking at these objections in a little detail, as for the power requirements, they are indeed formidable. Suppose we have a perfect rocket that expels reaction mass at the speed of light, in the form of pure energy. To reach 99 percent of that speed itself, the motors would have to spend about 13 tons of mass for each 1 ton of ship and payload. Furthermore, if the vessel is to slow down again, it must carry extra mass for that purpose. This does not merely double the fuel necessary, but squares it. So for every ton to be delivered at 99 percent of light speed, we need almost 200 tons of fuel! If the ship is to be of useful size, its motors must develop, quite literally, something like 100 trillion horsepower.

The thought seems altogether wild. Furthermore, to get the full benefit of the time shift, we would have to reach even higher speeds, such as 0.999 light. The requirements for this are downright ridiculous.

In short, a rocket that must carry all its own reaction mass will never come very near the speed of light.

Now suppose we had this same perfect spaceship and settled for a more reasonable pace, say one-fourth or one-half light. The mass needed would not be too much then. But the radiation still would be.

Space is almost empty, but not quite. We have mentioned the dusty, gassy regions called nebulae. They are far thinner than the atmosphere of Earth; we would call them good vacuums, except where they have begun condensing into stars and planets. Nevertheless, when they are light-years thick, they contain enough matter to block off the light of stars behind them. That is why we cannot see the center of our own galaxy.

Clear space has fewer atoms floating about than a nebula, but it does have some. They are mostly hydrogen. Between local stars, there are about fifteen such atoms per cubic inch. That is too little to observe directly—unless we move so fast that we strike billions of them per second. In that case, the effect is the same as if we were at rest and the atoms were driven against us at that speed. Energy is given off in the form of X-rays and other lethal radiation.

Plowing unprotected through the cosmos at a fourth light speed, we would soon be killed. Lead shielding would be of no real help. We would need too much. Besides, the hydrogen wind would erode it away.

For these reasons, conservative physicists do not believe men will ever travel faster than a few thousand miles per second. As we have seen, this means that it will take centuries to go from star to star, and without any noticeable time shrinkage.

The optimists retort: "Of course we don't yet know how. But there's no natural law that forbids us to make a screen against that hydrogen. And in fact, we can get work out of the stuff." By "screen," these men mean an extended field of electric and magnetic force. We have noted how useful such a thing would be to interplanetary craft. By deflecting charged particles at a considerable distance away from the hull, the force field would give protection against solar storms. Surely, as the vessels that ply the Solar System are improved, a screen generator will be developed.

So by the time man is ready for interstellar flight, he probably need not fear the hydrogen atoms he will meet. They are not

The "Crab" Nebula in Taurus is the remains of the explosion of a supernova observed by Chinese astronomers in A.D. *1054.*

charged like cosmic ray particles. But if no other trick will serve, a powerful electric field, laser beam, or the like can put a charge on them, well ahead of the ship. Then the magnetic screen can turn them aside.

This led a scientist named R. W. Bussard to another thought. As long as we must deflect the atoms anyway, why not use them for fuel and reaction mass?

Today, we cannot get energy from the hydrogen nucleus in a controlled fashion, only in the frightful explosion of a bomb. But researchers around the world are working on the problem. They are virtually certain to succeed. Then hydrogen atoms, tightly contained in electric and magnetic fields, will peacefully react with each other and give power to create, not destroy. Dr. Bussard proposes that this power be used to drive an intersteller spacecraft.

The ship will not scoop up gas in a ram jet made of metal. For one thing, the intake must be too wide, many miles across, for the method to work. The system will consist of the same screen fields that guard the crew. It will charge, capture, and compress the hydrogen that it encounters. Some gas will "burn" in a nuclear reaction. The energy thus gained will accelerate the rest of atoms backward, and thereby thrust the ship forward.

A Bussard vessel would not need to carry an undue amount of its own reaction mass or an impossibly powerful engine. It only has to get up to a fairly modest speed, at which it begins to meet a suitable number of atoms per second. Thereafter it rides free, so to speak. It can accelerate without limit, closer and closer to the velocity of light, shrinking the time within nearer and nearer to zero.

When the crew approach journey's end, they will reverse this process and spend about a year shedding that speed. Toward the end, they will have to stop the Bussard generators, which will not be taking in enough hydrogen any longer. By that time, though, they will be down to an interplanetary pace, and can finish the trip on their regular rockets.

Their ship will be a stupendous thing in full flight. Its energy of motion will be terrifying to contemplate, yet smoothly controlled by subtle and powerful machines. The crew will look out upon a universe hardly recognizable. Years, decades, centuries will pass in the cosmos while the ship's calendar marks a few weeks or months. Galactic reaches will separate the adventurers from the rest of mankind. But think what experiences, what glory will be theirs!

At present we have only the faintest inkling of how to build a craft like this. Maybe it is not possible after all. Certainly we will not develop the capability overnight.

Yet let us recall the history of the past hundred years and see how rapid progress can be. A century ago, Earth had no practical automobiles, powered aircraft, space vehicles, radio, television, electronic computers, household electricity, atomic energy, plastics, synthetic fabrics, medical X-rays, antibiotics, organ transplants and on and on through a breathtakingly long list. In fact, most of these things belong to the past fifty years, and many of them to the past twenty-five or ten.

If this trend continues, the next fifty years ought to see us on Pluto. With what we have learned from interplanetary ships, we should have a foundation on which to start developing interstellar argosies. That statement may be too optimistic. But what about a hundred years from now? Five hundred? A thousand? That is not so long on the scale of history. But it seems ample time for men to accomplish anything we can now imagine.

This brings up the question of what others, elsewhere in the universe, may already have done. If we are nothing unusual among intelligent races, which seems plausible, then doubtless

3160 YEARS to URANUS
1470 YEARS to SATURN
740 YEARS to JUPITER
76 YEARS to MARS
50 YEARS to VENUS

Fifty years ago trains were the fastest means of travel. Accordingly, an artist of the 1920's used them to show how much time a train, traveling a mile a minute, would require to reach the planets and the sun.

some are behind us in their technology, and some are ahead. That is, if interstellar travel is possible, there should be thinking creatures that are making such voyages today. They could have been doing so for thousands or even millions of years.

Then why have they not visited us?

The answer may lie quite simply in the sheer number of stars. Exploring this one galaxy would take tens of millions of years.

A "flying saucer" over New Mexico. There is no evidence that these are craft from another planet. But aliens may have visited Earth. . . .

The Solar System lies rather far out on the fringes. Perhaps the aliens have not gotten around to us yet. Or perhaps they have.

An expedition that landed here a million years ago would have found wilderness. Our ancestors had begun to use crude tools, but probably not fire. Their brains were small. They would have had nothing to say to beings that had built and manned a star ship.

If this happened, the strangers presumably noted something like, "Intelligent race evolving." They might not bother returning to see what happened next. We do not know how a nonhuman mind works.

Let us imagine, though, that this ancient civilizaton did care. With so many other planets to keep track of, it would not send anyone here often. But if some came back half a million years later, they found a species more advanced, larger-brained, maybe now a firemaker. By 30,000 B.C., or most likely earlier, modern types of man were in existence. The spacefarers might then decide to step up the pace of their visits a little. "Earth is getting more interesting all the time," they could think.

Was someone from another star, about the dawn of recorded history, responsible for legends that still linger? Were Oannes of Sumeria, or the beings that Ezekiel saw, or other gods and demigods, actually benevolent aliens? Will we someday find traces of them, like an abandoned camp on the far side of the moon? Are we due for another checkup any decade?

Ideas like these are farfetched. We should not take them too seriously. Nor should we swallow the claim that the so-called flying saucers are spaceships. There is no good evidence that they are, and plenty of evidence that they are not. To mention a single point, the reported behavior of flying saucers does not square with the laws of motion for solid objects.

The main reason for thus stirring up the imagination is to show how vast and mysterious the universe is, and how much we have to gain by venturing forth in it.

Out yonder, almost certainly, lie countless living worlds. Some of them are unclaimed. Once man has colonized these, he need not fear even the death of the sun. His race will survive. Other planets have natives that think. From them, man will learn what he might never discover for himself. And they in their turn will learn from him.

We need not wait for outside help. Humanity can embark alone on these great voyages, and meet its equals halfway. We stand in the dawn of a cosmic era. Whether it brightens into full day or not depends on us. People now alive can witness—can take part in—the exploration of the Solar System. Their children and grandchildren can take the first steps to the stars. If we have the will and the courage, our future in space is unlimited.

Bibliography

This is a brief selection from a very large literature and necessarily omits many excellent books. Titles marked with an asterisk (*) are especially suitable for younger readers.

Anderson, Poul, *Is There Life on Other Worlds?* New York: Crowell-Collier, 1963; rev. ed., Collier Books, 1968.

Asimov, Isaac. *Is Anyone There?* New York: Doubleday, 1967.

———. *The New Intelligent Man's Guide to Science.* New York: Basic Books, 1965.

Bergaust, Erik. *Reaching for the Stars.* New York: Doubleday, 1960.

Bova, Ben. *The Milky Way Galaxy.* New York: Holt, Rinehart & Winston, 1961.

Caidin, Martin. *Overture to Space.* New York: Duell, Sloan & Pierce, 1963.

Cameron, A. G. W. *Interstellar Communication.* New York: Benjamin, 1963.

Carpenter, M. Scott, *et al. We Seven, by the Astronauts Themselves.* New York: Simon & Schuster, 1962.

Clarke, Arthur C., and the editors of *Life*. *Man and Space*. New York: Time, Inc., 1964.

———. *Voices from the Sky*. New York: Harper & Row, 1965.

Dietz, David. *All About the Universe*. New York: Random House, 1965 (*).

Dole, S. H., and Asimov, Isaac. *Planets for Man*. New York: Random House, 1964.

Goodwin, Harold Leland. *Space: Frontier Unlimited*. Princeton, N.J.: Van Nostrand, 1962.

Hendrickson, Walter Brookfield. *Satellites and What They Do*. Indianapolis, Ind.: Bobbs-Merrill, 1963 (*).

Le Galley, Donald Paul (ed.). *Space Science*. New York: Wiley, 1963.

Leonov, A., and Sokolov, A. *The Stars Are Awaiting Us* (parallel Russian and English texts). Moscow: State Publication, 1967.

Ley, Willy (ed.). *Harnessing Space*. New York: Macmillan, 1963.

———. *Rockets, Missiles, and Space Travel*. New York: Viking, 1961.

———. *Missiles, Moonprobes, and Megaparsecs*. New York: New American Library, 1964.

Ley, Willy, and Bonestell, Chesley. *Beyond the Solar System*. New York: Viking, 1964.

———. *The Conquest of Space*. New York: Viking, 1950.

Ley, Willy, and Von Braun, Wernher. *The Exploration of Mars*. New York: Viking, 1956.

Lovell, Sir Alfred Charles Bernard. *The Exploration of Outer Space*. New York: Harper & Row, 1962.

Moore, Patrick. *A Guide to the Moon*. New York: Norton, 1953.

———. *A Guide to the Planets*. New York: Norton, 1954.

———. *Space in the Sixties*. Baltimore, Md.: Penguin, 1963.

Richardson, R. S. *The Fascinating World of Astronomy*. New York: McGraw-Hill, 1960.

Richardson, R. S., and Bonestell, Chesley. *Man and the Moon.* Cleveland: World, 1961.

———. *Mars.* New York: Harcourt, Brace & World, 1964.

Scharff, Robert. *Into Space with the Astronauts.* Columbus, Ohio: C. E. Merrill, 1965 (*).

Shklovskii, I. S., and Sagan, Carl. *Intelligent Life in the Universe.* San Francisco: Holden-Day, 1966.

Shternfeld, Ari. *Soviet Space Science* (U. S. Air Force translation). New York: Basic Books, 1959.

Spitz, Armand, and Gaynor, Frank. *Dictionary of Astronomy and Astronautics.* New York: Philosophical Library, 1959.

Sullivan, Walter. *We Are Not Alone* (rev. ed.). New York: New American Library, 1966.

Von Braun, Wernher, *Space Frontier.* New York: Holt, Rinehart & Winston, 1967.

Woodbury, David Oakes. *Outward Bound for Space.* Boston: Little, Brown, 1961.

Index

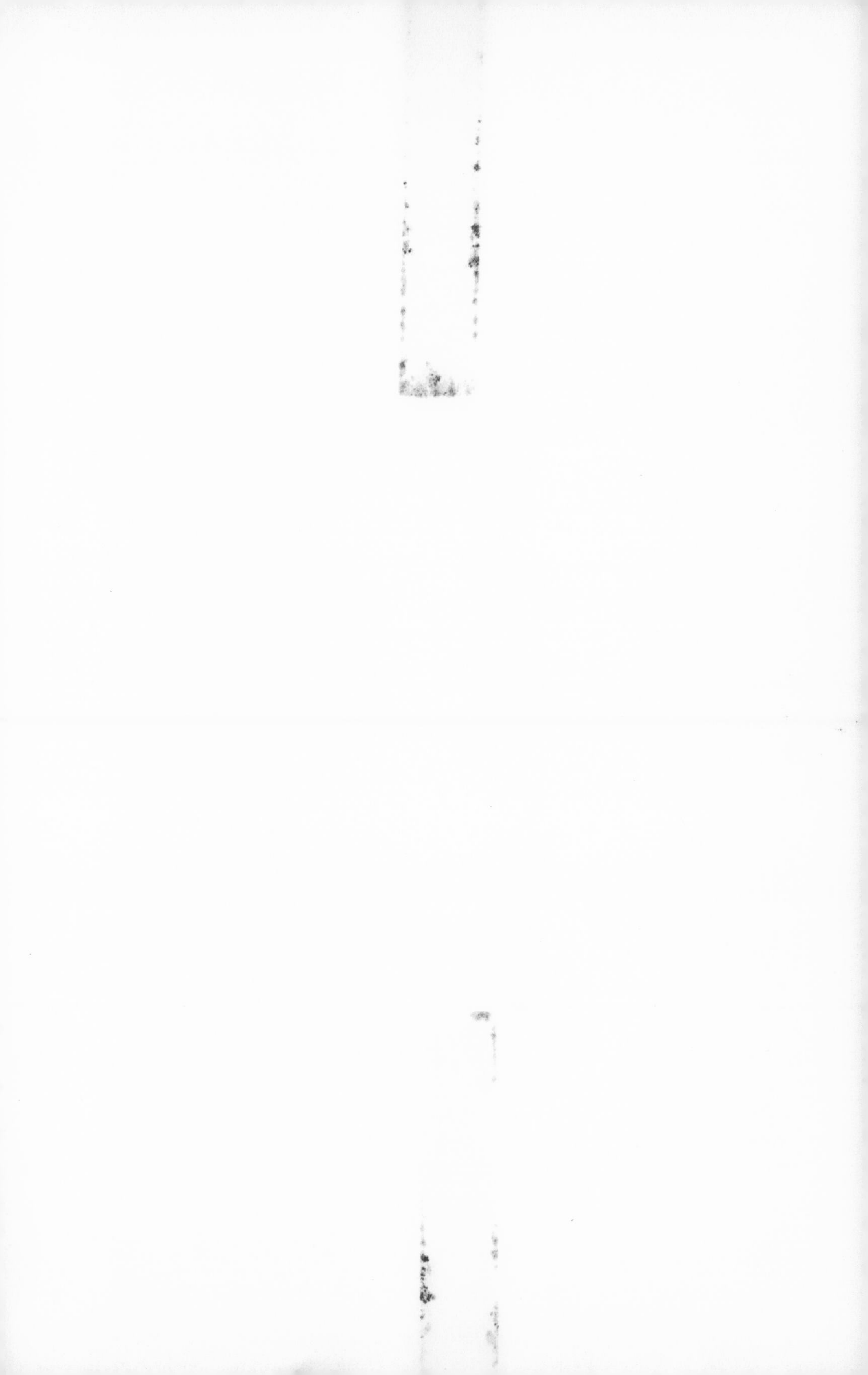

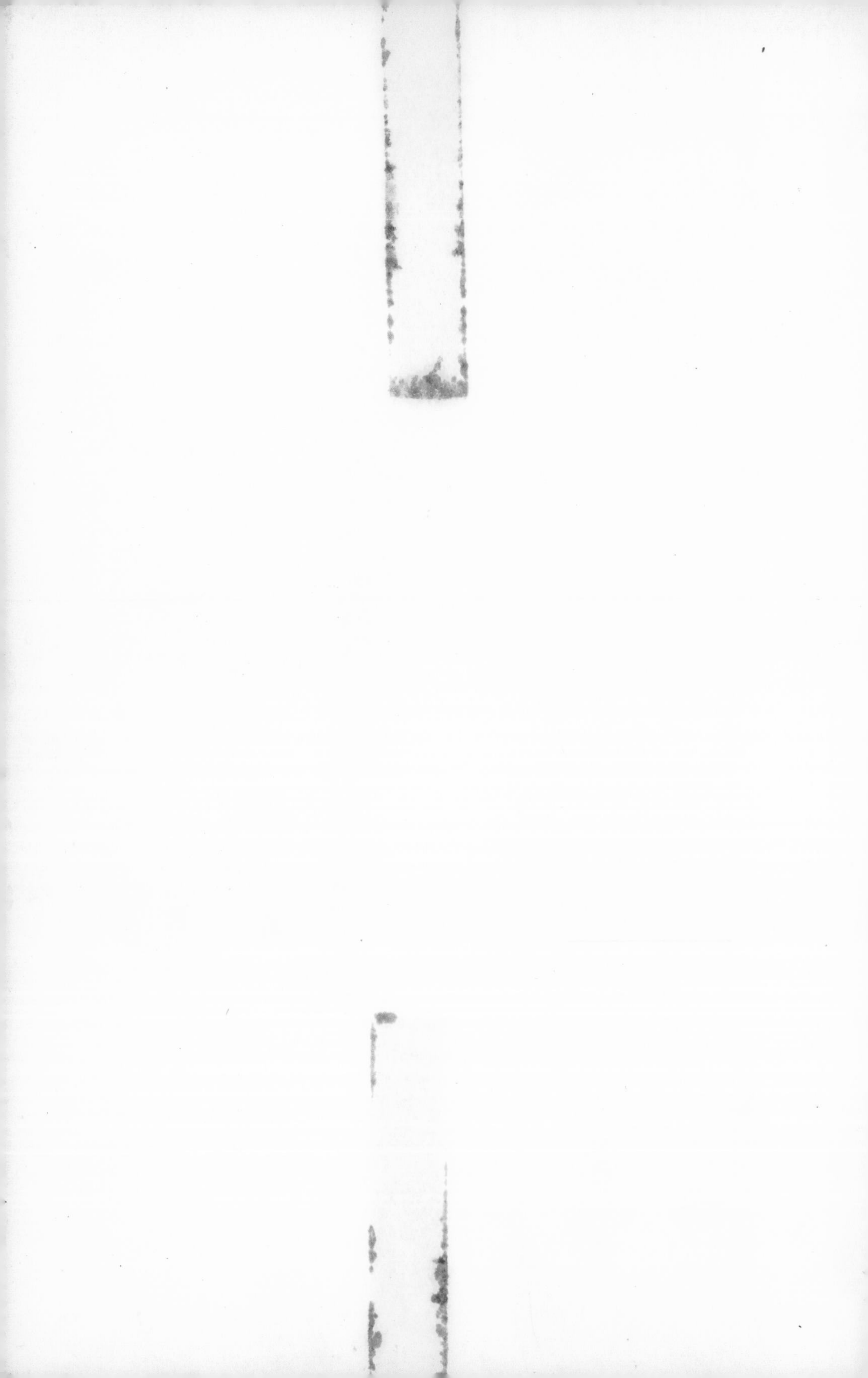